# Songs of
# Worship

# Songs of Worship

## Full Music

**Scripture Union**
130 City Road, London EC1V 2NJ

ISBN Nos:

| | |
|---|---|
| Full Music (cased) | 0 85421 865 3 |
| Full Music (cased, larger format) | 0 85421 896 3 |
| Full Music (limp) | 0 85421 897 1 |
| Melody (limp) | 0 85421 866 1 |
| Words (limp) | 0 85421 867 X |

Typesetting by Halstan & Co. Ltd., Amersham, Bucks.

Printed in Great Britain by McCorquodale (Newton) Ltd.,
Newton-le-Willows, Lancs.

# EDITOR'S INTRODUCTION

*We are living in a period of prolific hymn and song writing. The compiler of a hymnbook today has a wide range of living authors and composers to draw on, where his predecessor in the early and middle sixties had only a handful. Reflecting the questioning of social and political values, and the immense world changes taking place in short periods of time, the Christian culture of today is recoiling in attempts to update the general language of expression. Material is looked for in worship that relates to current experience rather than solely relying on the glories of the past. Images are drawn from industrial as well as agricultural experience, and mention of machines or the present world situation do not seem out of place.*

*This supplement brings together a wide variety of style and source. In the past such streams of creativity have been kept in isolated compartments. There are also some new marriages of words and music, and some music not normally associated with worship has been set to specifically Christian words, as for example Ron Pavey's 'O Lamb of God', which is set to a famous melody by Mozart.*

*The welcome trend towards the use of instruments other than the organ has been recognised by providing guitar chord symbols for many pieces, with a token keyboard realisation. Variety of style, texture, vocal requirements, and musical complexity is indeed a feature of the present collection. Users are encouraged to try this material and the settings provided, in instrumental and vocal versions suitable for their own situations. Our belief is that anything which seeks to widen the choice of media for congregational praise is pleasing to him who is the Giver of all Gifts.*

*Experimentation is the essence of life in any context, and this supplement provides an opportunity for it. Quite a large proportion of the material has already found a place in existing publications, and there is also a number of new and hitherto unpublished items. All the material has been well proven in church and fellowship situations, and the intention is that this supplement should be an offering to those in the church who wish to sample some of the considerable outpouring of songs of worship of recent years.*

*ROBIN SHELDON*

## PUBLISHER'S PREFACE

This supplement is published in the belief that it will prove ideal for virtually any church or fellowship. It will complement any existing hymnbook, so there is no need to discard the book already in use. It does not concentrate on any single tradition or style in present day Christian worship, but seeks to provide a collection useful to all types of church or fellowship, whether that group possesses a full organ or just a couple of guitars, and whether the circumstances are a stone cathedral, a wooden mission hall, or somebody's living room. It is our hope that people of all ages will be encouraged and excited by it, and that churches, fellowships, families and individuals will find it of value in many different worship situations, including family services, Bible services, youth services, communion services, house fellowship meetings, special occasions, camps and holiday activities, and many more.

SCRIPTURE UNION

# ACKNOWLEDGEMENTS

Permission to use copyright material is gratefully
acknowledged, and a list of copyright holders appears below.
Enquiries regarding copyright and reproduction of material in
this book should be made to Scripture Union. The publishers
apologise for any omissions or errors and undertake to rectify
any pointed out to them, in future editions of this songbook. In
some instances it has not been possible to identify or make
contact with owners of copyright, and these cases are also listed
below.

| WORDS | Hymn nos. |
|---|---|
| Boosey & Co. Ltd. | 14 |
| Broadman Press | 70 |
| Celebration Services International | 21, 55, 119 |
| Geoffrey Chapman, Publishers | 65 |
| Fishermen Inc. | 41, 106 |
| Franciscan Communications Centre | 111 |
| Galliards Ltd. | 2 (in USA), 6, 37 |
| Hinshaw Music Ltd. | 76 |
| Hye-Fye Music Ltd. | 12, 122 |
| Lexicon Music Inc. | 48 |
| Mayhew McCrimmon Ltd. | 83 |
| Oxford University Press | 18, 68, 78, 84, 97, 105 |
| Scripture Union | 19, 36 |
| Stainer & Bell Ltd. | 23, 25, 26, 57, 61, 67, 79, 81 |
| Thankyou Music | 86 (with author and composer) |
| Vanguard Music Ltd. | 110 |
| Joseph Weinberger Ltd. | 17, 50, 51, 59, 107 |
| The Word of God | 47 |

**Copyright in the words of the following hymns is held by
the authors:**

1, 2 (in UK), 3, 4, 5, 7–11, 13, 16, 20, 22, 24, 27–35, 38, 39,
40, 42–46, 49, 56, 58, 60, 62–64, 66, 69, 71–75, 77, 80, 86
(with Thankyou Music), 87–93, 95, 96, 98–104, 108, 112,
114–118, 120, 121, 123, 125–139.

# MUSIC

Agape Music Publishers 67
Boosey & Co. Ltd. 14
Broadman Press 70
Celebration Services International 55
Chappell & Co. Ltd. 127
J. Curwen & Son 74
Fishermen Inc. 41, 106
Franciscan Communications Centre 111
Galliard Ltd. 6, 37
Hinshaw Music 53, 76
Hye-Fye Music Ltd. 12, 122
Independent Press 73, 97
Lexicon Music Inc. 48
Novello & Co. 22 (i)
Oxford University Press 2, 3, 9, 19, 24, 57, 68, 81, 83, 96, 101, 103, 105, 108 (i)
Roberton Publications Ltd. 18, 38
Royal School of Church Music 75
St. Andrew Press 85
Rev. Dr. A. M. Smith 13
Stainer & Bell Ltd. 23, 25, 79
Thankyou Music 86 (with author & composer)
Vanguard Music Ltd. 110
Joseph Weinberger Ltd. 17, 50, 51, 59, 107

**Copyright in the music of the following hymns is held by the composers:**
5, 10, 15, 20, 21, 22 (ii), 26, 29–31, 34, 35 (ii), 39, 40, 42, 49, 58, 64, 69, 71, 78, 80, 84, 86 (with Thankyou Music), 87, 89, 91, 92 (i & ii), 95, 104, 112, 113, 115–118, 120, 121, 123, 124, 128, 130, 131, 134–139

**Apart from the following, copyright in all arrangements is held by the arranger:**
Celebration Services International 119
Oxford University Press 77
Betty Pulkingham 47
Scripture Union 36

**IT HAS NOT PROVED POSSIBLE TO TRACE THE COPYRIGHT HOLDERS OF THE FOLLOWING HYMNS:**
52, 82, 109

# CONTENTS

GOD THE FATHER                                    1–4
THE LORD JESUS CHRIST                             5–34
  His advent and second coming         5–9
  His incarnation: Christmas            10–14
  His life and ministry                 15–21
  His death and passion: Holy Week      22–26
  His resurrection: Easter              27–30
  Triumphant in Glory                   31–35
THE HOLY SPIRIT                                   36–42
  His nature                            36
  Pentecost, Whitsun                    37
  His renewing power                    38–42
THE TRINITY                                       43–44
THE CHURCH                                        45–81
  Worship and praise                    45–55
  Holy Communion                        56–61
  Renewal                               62–63
  Fellowship and unity                  64
  Outreach                              65–73
  Missionary                            74–75
  Stewardship                           76
  Man in God's Kingdom                  77
  Special days                          78–81
THE CHRISTIAN LIFE                                82–125
  Faith – love – joy – peace            82–88
  The Bible                             89–93
  Prayer                                94–98
  Repentance and forgiveness            99–100
  Healing                               101
  Testing-growth                        102–107
  Service and witness                   108–113
  Guidance and strength                 114–116
  Perseverance – dedication             117–119
  Giving                                120
  Searching for God                     121–122
  Freedom in Christ                     123
  The home                              124–125
GOD IN THE PSALMS: A SELECTION OF                 126–139
  PARAPHRASES

# 1

RUSSIAN ANTHEM      11.10.11.10.      A. Lvov (1799—1870)

*vvs. 2, 4, 5*

1 King of the universe, Lord of the ages,
   Maker of all things, Sustainer of life,
   Source of all power, all wisdom, and all justice,
   Hope of the nations, we praise and adore.

2 Powerful in majesty, throned in the heavens,
   Sun, moon and stars by your word are upheld,
   Time and Eternity kneel in your presence,
   Lord of the nations, we praise and adore.

3 Wisdom unsearchable, fathomless Knowledge,
   Past understanding by man's puny brain,
   Ordering all things from concept to fulfilment,
   Guide to the nations, we praise and adore.

4 Justice and Righteousness, holy, unswerving,
   All that is tainted shall burn in your flame,
   Bearing the sword against sin and corruption,
   Judge of the nations, we praise and adore.

5 Ruler and Potentate, Sage and Creator,
   Humbled before you, unworthy we bow,
   Yet we shall rise, cleansed from sin, freed from bondage,
   Merciful Father, we praise and adore.

MICHAEL SAWARD (b. 1932)

**2**

NEW HORIZONS  77.77.77.  Francis Westbrook (b. 1903)

*v. 4 see below

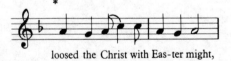

loosed the Christ with Eas-ter might,

# CREATOR

1 God of concrete, God of steel,
  God of piston and of wheel,
  God of pylon and of steam,
  God of girder and of beam,
  God of atom, God of mine,
  All the world of power is thine!

2 Lord of cable, Lord of rail,
  Lord of motorway and mail,
  Lord of rocket, Lord of flight,
  Lord of roaring satellite,
  Lord of lightning's livid line,
  All the world of speed is thine!

3 Lord of science, Lord of art,
  God of map and graph and chart,
  Lord of physics and research,
  Word of Bible, faith of Church,
  Lord of sequence and design,
  All the world of truth is thine!

4 God whose glory fills the earth
  Gave the universe its birth
  Loosed the Christ with Easter's might,
  Saves the world from evil's blight,
  Claims mankind by grace divine,
  All the world of love is thine!

RICHARD JONES

By permission of Oxford University Press

**3**

HIGHWOOD      11.10.11.10.      Richard Terry (1865—1938)

# CREATOR

1 O Lord of every shining constellation
   That wheels in splendour through the midnight sky;
   Grant us your spirit's true illumination
   To read the secrets of your work on high.

2 You, Lord, have made the atom's hidden forces,
   Your laws its mighty energies fulfil;
   Teach us, to whom you give such rich resources,
   In all we use, to serve your holy will.

3 O life, awakening in cell and tissue,
   From flower to bird, from beast to brain of man,
   Help us to trace, from birth to final issue,
   The sure unfolding of your age-long plan.

4 You, Lord, have stamped your image on your creatures,
   And though they mar that image, love them still.
   Lift up our eyes to Christ, that in his features
   We may discern the beauty of your will.

5 Great Lord of nature, shaping and renewing,
   You made us more than nature's sons to be;
   You help us tread, with grace our souls enduing,
   The road to life and immortality.

ALBERT BAYLY (b. 1901)

**4**

O QUANTA QUALIA    11.10.11.10.    La Feillée, Methode

## KINGDOM OF HEAVEN

1 Here from all nations, all tongues, and all peoples,
  Countless the crowd but their voices are one;
  Vast is the sight and majestic their singing—
  'God has the victory: he reigns from the throne!'

2 These have come out of the hardest oppression,
  Now they may stand in the presence of God,
  Serving their Lord day and night in his temple,
  Ransomed and cleansed by the Lamb's precious blood.

3 Gone is their thirst and no more shall they hunger,
  God is their shelter, his power at their side;
  Sun shall not pain them, no burning will torture,
  Jesus the Lamb is their Shepherd and Guide.

4 He will go with them to clear living water
  Flowing from springs which his mercy supplies;
  Gone is their grief and their trials are over,
  God wipes away every tear from their eyes.

5 Blessing and glory and wisdom and power
  Be to the Saviour again and again;
  Might and thanksgiving and honour for ever
  Be to our God: Hallelujah! Amen.

CHRISTOPHER IDLE (b. 1938)

# GOD THE FATHER

## SECOND TUNE

EPIPHANY HYMN      11.10.11.10.      Joseph Thrupp (1827—1867)

1 Here from all nations, all tongues, and all peoples,
  Countless the crowd but their voices are one;
  Vast is the sight and majestic their singing—
  'God has the victory: he reigns from the throne!'

2 These have come out of the hardest oppression,
  Now they may stand in the presence of God,
  Serving their Lord day and night in his temple,
  Ransomed and cleansed by the Lamb's precious blood.

3 Gone is their thirst and no more shall they hunger,
  God is their shelter, his power at their side;
  Sun shall not pain them, no burning will torture,
  Jesus the Lamb is their Shepherd and Guide.

4 He will go with them to clear living water
  Flowing from springs which his mercy supplies;
  Gone is their grief and their trials are over,
  God wipes away every tear from their eyes.

5 Blessing and glory and wisdom and power
  Be to the Saviour again and again;
  Might and thanksgiving and honour for ever
  Be to our God: Hallelujah! Amen.

CHRISTOPHER IDLE (b. 1938)

ADVENT PSALM        8 4 7 8 4 7        Norman Warren (b. 1934)

## An Advent Psalm

1 When the sun is darkened and the
    moon gives no light,
  And the stars fall from the sky,
  Then in heaven will appear the
    long-promised sign
  That proclaims the Son of Man.

2 All the peoples of the world will
    cry and lament
  When they see the Son of Man
  Coming in great power and glory
    high on the clouds
  With his angels serving him.

3 He will send his angels with a
    loud trumpet blast,
  From the farthest bounds of heaven;
  From the four winds they will gather
    his chosen ones
  Who are ready for their Lord.

4 None on earth can prophesy the
    day or the hour
  Which the Father knows alone;
  Keep awake and well prepared, for
    Jesus will come
  At the time you least expect.

5 Happy is the servant who is
    found at his work
  When his Master comes again;
  Heaven and earth will pass away, but
    never the words
  Of the Lord, the Son of Man.

CHRISTOPHER IDLE (b. 1938)

**6**

LET US SING      6 6 6 6 and refrain

here, ev - er near! Glo - ri - a in___

here, Christ is here, ev - er near! Glo - ri -

here, Christ is here, ev - er near!

[*rit. v.3 only*]

___ ex - cel - - - - sis.___

- a in ex - cel - - - sis. Glo - ri - a.

Glo - ri - a in ex - cel - sis. Glo - ri - a.

*Alternative tune—Theodoric, No. 18*

## ADVENT AND CHRISTMAS

1 Down to earth, as a dove,
 came to man holy love:
 Jesus Christ from above
 bringing great salvation
 meant for every nation.

 *Let us sing, sing, sing,*
 *Dance and spring, spring, spring;*
 *Christ is here,*
 *Ever near!*
 *Gloria in excelsis.*

2 This is love come to light,
 now is fear put to flight.
 God defeats darkest night;
 giving for our sorrows
 hope of new tomorrows.
 *Refrain*

3 Christ the Lord comes to feed
 hungry men in their need;
 in the house there is bread:*
 Jesus in a stable,
 in the church a table.
 *Refrain*

FRED KAAN (b. 1929)

*Bethlehem = house of bread*

# LORD JESUS CHRIST

*alternative version for v.2 (unacc.)*

*Slightly slower*

verse 2     S.T. unis

This is love, come to light, now is fear___ put to flight. God de - feats dark - est night; giv - ing for our sor - rows hope of new to - mor - rows. *Refrain* Let us sing, sing,

A.B. unis.

This is love come to light, now is fear___ put to flight. God de - feats dark - est night; giv - ing for our sor - rows hope of new to - mor - rows.___ *Refrain* Let us sing,

# ADVENT AND SECOND COMING

sing, Dance and spring, spring, spring;

sing, sing, Dance and spring, spring, spring;

Christ is here, ev – er

Christ is here, Christ is here, ev – er

near! Glo – ri – a in ex – cel –

near! Glo – ri – a in ex –

– – – – sis.

– cel – – – – sis, Glo – ri – a.

# LORD JESUS CHRIST

**7**

BUNESSAN    Irregular    Old Gaelic Melody

*An alternative arrangement can be found under No. 8*

SECOND TUNE

DAYS OF JESUS    Irregular    Helen Wickham (b. 1949)

## ADVENT AND SECOND COMING

*Commas fall at the end of every second line of words*

1 Bethlehem waiting,
  Joseph and Mary,
  Finding a stable,
  Sleep in the hay.
  Angels are singing,
  Shepherds are watching,
  Jesus is sleeping,
  Joyful the day.

2 Valleys shall echo
  Hung between mountains,
  Shaken with thunder
  Covered with snow.
  Satan is conquered
  Evil is broken
  Jesus has risen
  Worship the day.

3 Souls are awaking
  Clouds are descending,
  Sunshine is breaking,
  Clouds melt away.
  Promise fulfilling,
  Jesus returning,
  Raising the living,
  Soon is the day.

4 Sorrow and sighing
  Seen in our faces,
  Anguish and dying,
  Banished away.
  Christians are rising,
  Glory is waiting,
  Jesus is coming,
  Watch for the day.

CHRISTOPHER PORTEOUS (b. 1935)

**8**

BUNESSAN
Irregular
Old Gaelic Melody

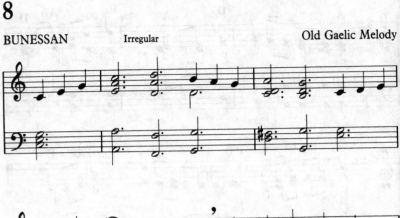

*Commas fall at the end of every second line of words*

*An alternative arrangement can be found under No. 7*

1 Angels are bringing
  news in the morning;
  splendour from heaven
  lights up the sky.
  Can we envisage
  Bethlehem's baby
  grown up to manhood,
  led out to die?

2 Angels are telling:
  Now he is risen!
  See where they laid him —
  empty it stands.
  Can we believe it
  till we have seen him,
  till he has shown us
  scars on his hands?

3 Angels are calling:
  He is returning!
  Day of our judgement
  dawning at last.
  Can we imagine
  how we shall face him,
  fearing the future,
  fleeing the past?

4 Lord of the angels,
  baby no longer,
  star of our morning,
  shine on our way.
  Crucified Saviour,
  risen Redeemer,
  King of all glory,
  save us today!

CHRISTOPHER IDLE (b. 1938)

**9**

CUDDESDON　　　6 5 6 5 D　　　W. H. Ferguson (1874–1950)

CUDDESDON–By permission of Oxford University Press

1 Christ is surely coming bringing his reward,
  Omega and Alpha, First and Last and Lord:
  Root and stem of David, brilliant morning star:
  Meet your Judge and Saviour, nations near and far!
  Meet your Judge and Saviour, nations near and far!

2 See the holy city! There they enter in,
  Men by Christ made holy, washed from every sin:
  Thirsty ones, desiring all he loves to give,
  Come for living water, freely drink, and live!
  Come for living water, freely drink, and live!

3 Grace be with God's people! Praise his holy name!
  Father, Son, and Spirit, evermore the same.
  Hear the certain promise from the eternal home:
  'Surely I come quickly!' — Come, Lord Jesus, come!
  'Surely I come quickly!' — Come, Lord Jesus, come!

CHRISTOPHER IDLE (b. 1938)

# 10

LORD JESUS CHRIST

CALYPSO CAROL     Irregular     Michael Perry (b. 1942)
arr. *Stephen Coates*

*Choruses*

1 See him a-lying on a bed of straw;
   A draughty stable with an open door;
   Mary cradling the Babe she bore;
   The Prince of Glory is his name.
     *O now carry me to Bethlehem*
     *To see the Lord appear to men:*
     *Just as poor as was the stable then,*
     *The Prince of Glory when he came.*

2 Star of silver sweep across the skies,
   Show where Jesus in the manger lies,
   Shepherds swiftly from your stupor rise
   To see the Saviour of the world.
     *Chorus*

3 Angels, sing again the song you sang,
   Bring God's glory to the heart of man:
   Sing that Bethlem's little Baby can
   Be salvation to the soul.
     *Chorus*

4 Mine are riches — from thy poverty:
   From thine innocence, eternity;
   Mine, forgiveness by thy death for me,
   Child of sorrow for my joy.
     *Chorus*

MICHAEL PERRY (b. 1942)

# 11

**LONDONDERRY AIR**  11.10.11.10.D

Irish Traditional Melody
*arr. by Robin Sheldon (b. 1932)*

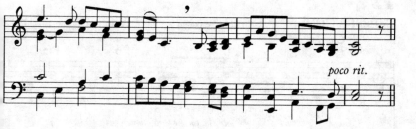

1 O Son of God we too would gather round you
  Like those who gathered round your manger bed,
  Summoned by choirs of angel hosts from heaven
  Like kings who came, who were by starlight led.
  Like them we gaze in awe and adoration
  To see the baby born in Bethlehem.
  He took our flesh, he shared our human sorrows
  His birth reveals God's love, God's peace to sinful men.

2 O lamb of God we too would kneel before you
  As shepherds knelt on that first Christmas morn
  Hearing the songs of angel choirs in heaven
  Who bring their praise, for Christ the King is born.
  Like them we come to bring our praise and worship,
  For God is here, we greet him face to face.
  Behold his love within a lowly manger
  Much more then we deserve, here lies his wondrous grace.

3 O Son of man, we too would seek your presence
  As long ago men thronged your earthly days
  Seeking your help, your miracles of healing
  By quiet lake in busy city ways.
  Like them we come our varied burdens bearing
  Knowing that you and you alone can heal,
  Needing your healing touch, your words of comfort
  To every seeking heart yourself dear Lord reveal.

CHRISTOPHER PORTEOUS (b. 1935)

*An adaptation and revision of a poem by Faith A. E. Brettell*

# LORD JESUS CHRIST

**12**

CELEBRATIONS     11.14. and refrain     Valerie Collison (b. 1933)

Come and join the cel - e - bra - tion, It's a ve - ry spe-cial day; Come and share our ju - bi -la - tion, There's a new King born to-day! See the shep - herds hur - ry down to Beth - le - hem; Gaze in

## HIS INCARNATION—CHRISTMAS

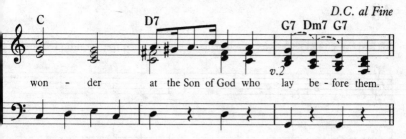

won - der    at the Son of God who    lay be - fore them.

*Come and join the celebration,*
*It's a very special day;*
*Come and share our jubilation,*
*There's a new King born today!*

1 See the shepherds hurry down to Bethlehem;
   Gaze in wonder at the Son of God who lay before them.
   *Chorus*

2 Wise men journey, led to worship by a star,
   Kneel in homage, bringing gifts from lands afar, so,
   *Chorus*

3 'God is with us,' round the world the message bring,
   He is with us, 'Welcome', all the bells on earth are pealing.
   *Chorus*

VALERIE COLLISON (b. 1933)

# 13

SURSUM CORDA      10.10.10.10.      Alfred Smith (1879—1971)

*Commas fall at the end of every second line of words*

1 Had he not loved us
   he had never come,
Yet is he love
   and love is all his way:
Low to the mystery
   of the virgin's womb
Christ bows his glory —
   born on Christmas Day.

2 Had he not loved us
   He had never come;
Had he not come
   He need have never died
Nor won the victory
   of the vacant tomb,
The awful triumph
   of the Crucified.

3 Had he not loved us
   He had never come;
Still were we lost
   in sorrow, sin and shame,
The doors fast shut
   on our eternal home
Which now stand open —
   for he loved and came.

TIMOTHY DUDLEY-SMITH (b. 1926)

**14**

BABY BOY

10.10.10.9 and Refrain

Edric Connor Collection
*arr. D. J. Crawshaw (b. 1947)*

## HIS INCARNATION—CHRISTMAS

*last time—rit.*

1 The Virgin Mary had a baby boy,
  The Virgin Mary had a baby boy,
  The Virgin Mary had a baby boy,
  And they say that his name was Jesus.
    *He come from the glory*
    *He come from the glorious kingdom;*
    *He come from the glory*
    *He come from the glorious kingdom;*
    *Oh, yes! believer.*
    *Oh, yes! believer.*
    *He come from the glory*
    *He come from the glorious kingdom.*

2 The angels sang when the babe was born,
  The angels sang when the babe was born,
  The angels sang when the babe was born,
  And proclaimed him the Saviour Jesus.
    *Chorus*

3 The wise men saw where the babe was born,
  The wise men saw where the babe was born,
  The wise men saw where the babe was born,
  And they saw that his name was Jesus.
    *Chorus*

from the EDRIC CONNOR Collection

**15**

COME AND PRAISE 11.11.—11.11. (D.C. Chorus)     *Trad., arr. by P. C. Butler and David Wilson (b. 1940)*

*Come and praise the Lord our King,*
*Hallelujah,*
*Come and praise the Lord our King,*
*Hallelujah.*

1 Christ was born in Bethlehem, Hallelujah,
   Son of God and Son of Man, Hallelujah:
   *Chorus*

2 He grew up an earthly child, Hallelujah,
   Of the world, but undefiled, Hallelujah:
   *Chorus*

3 Jesus died at Calvary, Hallelujah,
   Rose again triumphantly, Hallelujah:
   *Chorus*

4 He will cleanse us from our sin, Hallelujah,
   If we live by faith in him, Hallelujah.
   *Chorus*

5 We will live with him one day, Hallelujah,
   And for ever with him stay, Hallelujah:
   *Chorus*

ANON

*The chorus may be omitted after verses 1, 2, 3 and 4 if a shorter version is required.*

**16**

LORD OF LORDS      6 7 7 5

Traditional Melody
© arr. Anthony Leach (b. 1947)

1 Jesus Christ, Son of God,
  Christ who calmed the cruel sea,
  Christ by whom the stars were made,
  Christ, you care for me.

2 Jesus Christ, way to God,
  Wholly good, wholly right,
  By comparison I am
  Darkness in your light.

3 Jesus Christ, Lord of truth,
  Blow illusions all away,
  Show me, sinner that I am,
  Death should be my pay.

4 Jesus Christ, hammered, nailed
  At a point in time and space,
  To a rough-hewn cross of wood,
  Died there in my place.

5 Jesus Christ, Prince of life,
  Bursting from your borrowed grave,
  Put to death, you've beaten death,
  Yours the power to save.

6 Jesus Christ, hear my prayer,
  Voice of all my pride, be dumb.
  Lord, I turn from all that's wrong,
  Trustingly I come.

7 Jesus Christ, Saviour, God,
  Give your Spirit, Lord, to me,
  Drown my sins in ocean deeps,
  Make me truly free.

8 Jesus Christ, Lord of lords,
  Lord of choices great and small,
  Lord of leisure, work and love,
  Lord, I give you all.

MICHAEL HEWS (b. 1925)

# LORD JESUS CHRIST

HENFIELD  Irregular  Patrick Appleford (b. 1924)

*intro. to v. 1 only*

*vv. 1–4*  *last verse*
(optional for
others)

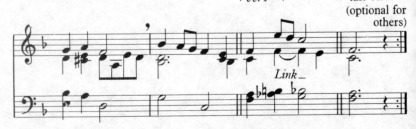

*Link*

## HIS LIFE AND MINISTRY

1 Jesus our Lord, our King and our God,
    ruling in might and love,
All power on earth is given to you,
you are our King above;
Help us to use the power you give,
Humbly to order how men live.
*Lord, we are called to follow you;*
*This we ask strength to do.*

2 Jesus our Lord, and humblest of Priests,
    doing your Father's will;
Suffering servant, working with men,
    your work continues still.
Help us to offer in our prayer,
All of our work and service here.
*Lord, we are called to follow you;*
*This we ask strength to do.*

3 Jesus our Lord, and Shepherd of men,
    caring for human needs;
Feeding the hungry, healing the sick,
    showing your love in deeds;
Help us in your great work to share;
People in want still need your care.
*Lord, we are called to follow you;*
*This we ask strength to do.*

4 Jesus our Lord, and Prophet of God,
    preaching his mighty plan,
You are the Way, the Truth and the Life,
    teaching the mind of man;
Help us in all our words to show
You are the truth men need to know.
*Lord, we are called to follow you;*
*This we ask strength to do.*

5 Jesus our Lord, our God and our Priest,
    Prophet and Shepherd-King,
Yours is the kingdom, glory and power,
    yours is the praise we sing.
Leader of men, you show the way
We are to follow day by day.
*Glorious God, we follow you;*
*This you give strength to do.*

PATRICK APPLEFORD (b. 1924)

# 18

**THEODORIC**     6 6 6 6 6 and Refrain     Melody from Piae Cantiones
*arr. Gustav Holst (1874—1934)*

1 God is love: his the care,
   Tending each, everywhere.
   God is love — all is there!
   Jesus came to show him,
   That mankind might know him:
     *Sing aloud, loud, loud!*
     *Sing aloud, loud, loud!*
     *God is good!*
     *God is truth! God is beauty! Praise him!*

2 Jesus lived here for men,
   Strove and died, rose again,
   Rules our hearts, now as then;
   For he came to save us
   By the truth he gave us:
     *Sing aloud . . .*

3 To our Lord praise we sing —
   Light and life, friend and king,
   Coming down love to bring,
   Pattern for our duty,
   Showing God in beauty:
     *Sing aloud . . .*

PERCY DEARMER

*originally in the key of F minor*

**19**

TYROL       D C M                              Tyrolean Melody

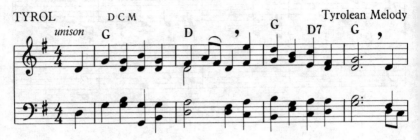

1 A Man once came from Galilee,
No Man so great as he.
We left our work and went with him,
His followers to be.
Lord Jesus, be our Teacher now,
And may we learn from you
To love and serve the Father God
And other people, too.

2 We saw our Master heal the sick;
We saw his love for men.
We saw his power reach out to touch
And bring to life again.
Lord Jesus, be our Healer now,
And make us whole and strong
That we may share your love and power
And serve you all day long.

3 They nailed him to a cross of wood;
They scoffed and watched him die.
And we could not at first believe
That he would reign on high.
Lord Jesus, be our Saviour now,
And may we all repent
And hate the sin that brought you down
To bear our punishment.

4 We saw the stone was rolled away
Before the empty grave.
We met the risen Lord of life,
The one who came to save.
Lord Jesus, you are God and King;
Oh, may we all obey
And glorify you, risen Lord,
In all we do each day.

MARGARET OLD (b. 1932)

(The first half of each verse can be sung by a small group representing disciples,
everyone else then singing the second half of each verse.)

Words by permission of Scripture Union from *Sing to God*
Music harmony as in *BBC Hymn Book* by permission of Oxford University Press

**20**

JESUS FROM GLORY   10.7 10.8   Michael A. Baughan (b. 1930)
and David G. Wilson (b. 1940)

1 Jesus from glory to Bethlehem came,
  Born in a small wayside inn;
  He who created the worlds by his pow'r
  In grace came to save us from sin.

2 Jesus the Word to his own people came,
  Their true Redeemer and King,
  Him they rejected, his truth they despised,
  They spurned all the gifts he would bring.

3 Jesus the Saviour to Calvary came,
  Victim of hatred and strife;
  Flogged and disowned he was nailed to a cross,
  And yet by that death we have life.

4 Jesus the Lord out of death's bondage came,
  Victor o'er Satan and sin,
  Now in his pow'r he will dwell in our lives,
  And help us our vict'ry to win.

5 Jesus the Master to your life will come,
  Bringing salvation and peace;
  In his glad service you'll find your reward
  And pleasures that never shall cease.

6 Jesus the Sovereign in glory shall come,
  Man's full redemption to bring;
  Saints of all ages their Lord shall acclaim,
  Their Saviour, their God and their King.

JIM SEDDON (b. 1915)

© J. E. Seddon and M. A. Baughen 1969. By kind permission.

**21**

WHAT A GIFT    Irregular

Pat Uhl Howard
Arr. Betty Pulkingham (b. 1928)

**Joyfully, with a driving rhythm**

*Refrain*

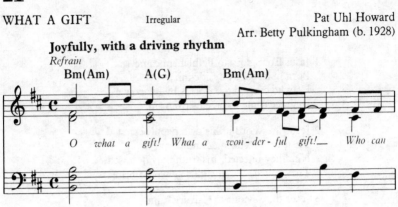

O what a gift! What a won-der-ful gift!___ Who can

tell    the won-ders of the Lord?    Let us

o - pen our eyes    our ears and our hearts; It

## HIS LIFE AND MINISTRY

A(G)     Bm(Am)     Fine

Christ the Lord, it is he!

Verses     Bm(Am)

1 In the still - ness of the night___ when the
2 On the night be - fore he died___ it was
3 On the hill of Cal - va - ry___ the
4 Ear - ly on that morn - ing when the
5 Some day with the saints ___ we will

A(G)     G(F)     A(G)

world was a - sleep,__ the al - migh - ty ___ word__ leapt __
Pass - ov - er night,__ and he gath - ered his friends to -
world__ held its breath,__ for__ there for the world to__
guards were sleep-ing, back to life came
come be - fore our Fa - ther,__ and then we will shout and dance and

# LORD JESUS CHRIST

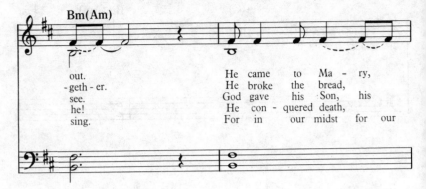

out.
-geth-er.
see.
he!
sing.

He came to Ma - ry,
He broke the bread,
God gave his Son, his
He con - quered death,
For in our midst for our

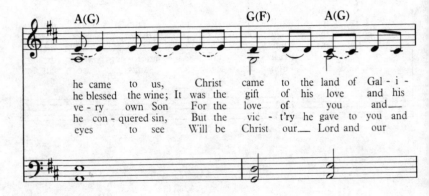

he came to us, Christ came to the land of Gal - i -
he blessed the wine; It was the gift of his love and his
ve - ry own Son For the love of you and
he con - quered sin, But the vic - t'ry he gave to you and
eyes to see Will be Christ our Lord and our

*D.C.*
*Refrain*

- lee.
life.
me.
me!
King.

Christ our Lord and our King!

# HIS LIFE AND MINISTRY

*O what a gift! What a wonderful gift!*
*Who can tell the wonders of the Lord?*
*Let us open our eyes our ears and our hearts;*
*It is Christ the Lord, it is he!*

1 In the stillness of the night when the world was
    asleep, the almighty word leapt out.
  He came to Mary, he came to us,
  Christ came to the land of Galilee.
  Christ our Lord and our King!
    *Refrain*

2 On the night before he died it was Passover
    night, and he gathered his friends together.
  He broke the bread, he blessed the wine;
  It was the gift of his love and his life.
  Christ our Lord and our King!
    *Refrain*

3 On the hill of Calvary the world held its breath,
    for there for the world to see.
  God gave his Son, his very own Son
  For the love of you and me.
  Christ our Lord and our King!
    *Refrain*

4 Early on that morning when the guards were
    sleeping, back to life came he!
  He conquered death, he conquered sin,
  But the victory he gave to you and me!
  Christ our Lord and King!
    *Refrain*

5 Some day with the saints we will come before
    our Father, and then we will shout and
    dance and sing.
  For in our midst for our eyes to see
  Will be Christ our Lord and our King!
  Christ our Lord and our King!
    *Refrain*

PAT UHL HOWARD

FIRST TUNE

**22**

**LYNDHURST**  6 5 6 5 D  Frederick William Blunt (1839—1921)

*SHORTER ALTERNATIVE*
*Verses 1 and 2 (and 3, if desired) may be used in 4-line stanzas as a complete hymn, and may then be sung to the tune 'Green Hill'*

## SECOND TUNE

**GREEN HILL**    6 5 6 5                    Robin Sheldon (b. 1932)

1 At the cross of Jesus
  I would take my place
  Drawn by such a measure
  Of redeeming grace.
  Fill my heart with sorrow,
  Lift my eyes to see,
  Jesus Christ my Saviour
  Crucified for me.

2 At the cross of Jesus
  Patiently he bore
  Bitter shame and sorrow,
  Grief and anguish sore.
  Through eternal ages
  I shall never know
  What he had to suffer,
  Why he loved me so.

3 At the Cross of Jesus,
  Even though I be
  Chief of all the sinners
  There is hope for me.
  Judged, condemned and
                      guilty,
  I am lost indeed,
  But the cross of Jesus
  Meets my deepest need.

4 At the cross of Jesus
  Pardon is complete;
  Love and justice mingle,
  Truth and mercy meet.
  Though my sins condemn
                        me,
  Jesus died instead;
  There is full forgiveness
  In the blood he shed.

5 At the cross of Jesus,
  You have set me free,
  So I come, dear Saviour,
  Yielding all to thee.
  Let your love possess me,
  So that all may see
  What your death accomplished
  On the cross for me.

JOHN EDDISON (b. 1916)

**23**

LORD OF THE DANCE     Irregular

Shaker Tune
*Adapted by Sydney Carter (1915)*

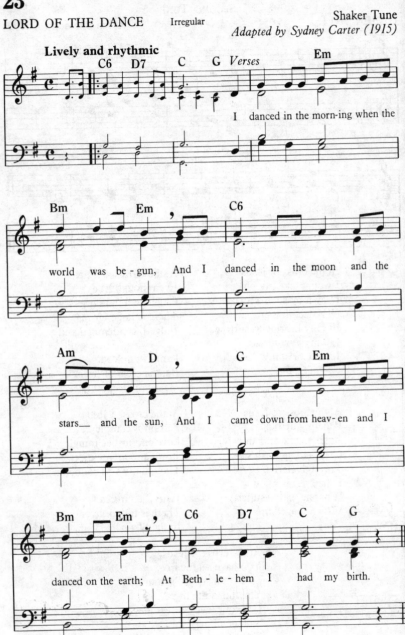

I danced in the morn-ing when the world was be-gun, And I danced in the moon and the stars__ and the sun, And I came down from heav-en and I danced on the earth; At Beth-le-hem I had my birth.

# HIS DEATH AND PASSION—HOLY WEEK

Refrain

Dance then wher-ev-er you may be;
I am the Lord of the Dance, said he, And I'll
lead you all, wher-ev-er you may be, And I'll
lead you all in the dance, said he. dance, said he.

# LORD JESUS CHRIST

*Melody for last verse*

They cut me down and I leap up high;

I am the life that-'ll nev-er, nev-er die;

I'll live in you if you'll live in me:

I am the Lord of the Dance, said he.

1 I danced in the morning
   when the world was begun,
And I danced in the moon
   and the stars and the sun,
And I came down from heaven
   and I danced on the earth;
At Bethlehem
   I had my birth.
*Dance then wherever you may be;*
*I am the Lord of the Dance, said he,*
*And I'll lead you all, wherever you may be,*
*And I'll lead you all in the dance, said he.*

2 I danced for the scribe
 and the pharisee,
But they would not dance
 and they wouldn't follow me;
I danced for the fishermen,
 for James and John;
They came with me
 and the dance went on:
 *Refrain*

3 I danced on the Sabbath
 and I cured the lame:
The holy people
 said it was a shame.
They whipped and they stripped
 and they hung me high,
And they left me there
 on a cross to die:
 *Refrain*

4 I danced on a Friday
 when the sky turned black;
It's hard to dance
 with the devil on your back.
They buried my body
 and they thought I'd gone;
But I am the dance
 and I still go on:
 *Refrain*

5 They cut me down
 and I leap up high;
I am the life
 that'll never, never die;
I'll live in you
 if you'll live in me:
I am the Lord
 of the Dance, said he:
 *Refrain*

SYDNEY CARTER (b. 1915)
used with permission of Stainer and Bell

# 24

**DOWN AMPNEY**     6 6 11.D     R. Vaughan Williams (1872–1958)

*This tune was composed for R. F. Littledale's hymn 'Come down, O love divine', in the English Hymnal 1906.*

1 Lord of the cross of shame,
  Set my cold heart aflame
  With love for you, my Saviour and my Master;
  Who on that lonely day
  Bore all my sins away,
  And saved me from the judgment and disaster.

2 Lord of the empty tomb,
  Born of a virgin's womb,
  Triumphant over death, its power defeated;
  How gladly now I sing
  Your praise, my risen King,
  And worship you, in heaven's splendour seated.

3 Lord of my life today,
  Teach me to live and pray
  As one who knows the joy of sins forgiven;
  So may I ever be,
  Now and eternally,
  United with the citizens of heaven.

MICHAEL SAWARD (b. 1932)

WERE YOU THERE        10.10.14.10.        Negro Spiritual
*arr. by Angela Reith*

1 Were you there when they crucified my Lord?
Were you there when they crucified my Lord?
Oh! Sometimes it causes me to tremble, tremble, tremble.
Were you there when they crucified my Lord?

2 Were you there when they nailed him to the tree?
Were you there when they nailed him to the tree?
Oh! Sometimes it causes me to tremble, tremble, tremble.
Were you there when they nailed him to the tree?

3 Were you there when they pierced him in the side?
Were you there when they pierced him in the side?
Oh! Sometimes it causes me to tremble, tremble, tremble.
Were you there when they pierced him in the side?

4 Were you there when the sun refused to shine?
Were you there when the sun refused to shine?
Oh! Sometimes it causes me to tremble, tremble, tremble.
Were you there when the sun refused to shine?

5 Were you there when they laid him in the tomb?
Were you there when they laid him in the tomb?
Oh! Sometimes it causes me to tremble, tremble, tremble.
Were you there when they laid him in the tomb?

6 Were you there when he rose up from the dead?
Were you there when he rose up from the dead?
Oh! Sometimes I feel like shouting glory, glory, glory.
Were you there when he rose up from the dead?

ANON

# LORD JESUS CHRIST

DO YOU SEE THAT MAN  10.8 10.8

Alan Thomas
arr. John Lockley

1. Do you see that ___ man ___

*The guitar and piano should not play together in this item since the chords given in the keyboard arrangement are different from those indicated for guitar.*

they've just ar - re - sted, The one they're

ta, - - - king off to try? He came to us,

He came to us, but we did-n't

# LORD JESUS CHRIST

want      him,           And so it   seems

_____ that he must    die.

*after final verse*

1 Do you see that man they've just arrested,
  The one they're taking off to try?
  He came to us, but we didn't want him,
  And so it seems that he must die.

2 Do you see that man, the one who's stumbling,
  As all the people jeer and hiss?
  He told us all we should love our neighbours;
  We didn't care, so we did this.

3 Do you see that man who can forgive them,
  While nails are biting through his bone?
  We didn't want his whole new order,
  We wanted to be left alone.

4 Do you see that man, the one who's hanging
  Upon the cross, and almost dead?
  He showed us truth, but the vision scared us,
  So we showed him a cross instead.

5 Even now we can't avoid his questions,
  Although we want to run and hide,
  He rose again, and we can't forget him,
  For it was by our hands he died.

PETER CASEY

EPIPHANY HYMN     11.10.11.10.     Joseph Thrupp (1827—1867)

*vvs. 1, 3, 4, 5*     *vvs. 1, 5*

1 These are the facts as we have received them,
 These are the truths that the Christian believes,
 This is the basis of all our preaching,
 Christ died for sinners and rose from the tomb.

2 These are the facts as we have received them,
 Christ has fulfilled what the Scriptures foretold,
 Adam's whole family in death had been sleeping,
 Christ through his rising restores us to life.

3 These are the facts as we have received them,
 We, with our Saviour, have died on the Cross,
 Now, having risen, our Jesus lives in us,
 Gives us his Spirit and makes us his home. .

4 These are the facts as we have received them,
 We shall be changed in the blink of an eye,
 Trumpets shall sound as we face life immortal,
 This is the victory through Jesus, our Lord.

5 These are the facts as we have received them,
 These are the truths that the Christian believes,
 This is the basis of all our preaching,
 Christ died for sinners and rose from the tomb.

MICHAEL SAWARD (b. 1932)

**28**

ST. GERTRUDE      6 5 6 5 Triple      Arthur Sullivan (1842—1900)

*Refrain*

1 Jesus, Prince and Saviour,
　Lord of life who died:
　Christ, the friend of sinners,
　Sinners crucified.
　For a lost world's ransom
　All himself he gave,
　Lay at last death's victim
　Lifeless in the grave.

　　*Lord of life triumphant,*
　　*Risen now to reign!*
　　*King of endless ages,*
　　*Jesus lives again!*

2 In his power and Godhead
　Every victory won,
　Pain and passion ended,
　All his purpose done:
　Christ the Lord is risen!
　Sighs and sorrows past,
　Death's dark night is over,
　Morning comes at last!
　　*Refrain*

3 Resurrection morning!
　Sinners' bondage freed.
　Christ the Lord is risen—
　He is risen indeed!
　Jesus, Prince and Saviour,
　Lord of life who died,
　Christ the King of glory
　Now is glorified!
　　*Refrain*

TIMOTHY DUDLEY-SMITH (b. 1926)

**29**

SOUND OF WIND      66.86.66.      Robin Sheldon (b. 1932)

1 This day above all days
　Glad hymns of triumph bring;
　Lift every heart to love and praise
　And every voice to sing:
　For Jesus is risen
　Our glorious Lord and King!

2 Christ keeps his Eastertide!
　The Father's power descends;
　The shuttered tomb he opens wide,
　The rock-hewn grave he rends:
　For Jesus is risen
　And death's dominion ends!

3 What sovereign grace is found
　In Christ for all our need!
　The powers of sin and death are bound,
　The ransomed captives freed:
　For Jesus is risen
　The Prince of Life indeed!

4 So lift your joyful songs
　With all the hosts on high,
　Where angel and archangel throngs
　His ceaseless praises cry:
　For Jesus is risen
　And lives no more to die!

TIMOTHY DUDLEY-SMITH (b. 1926)

# 30

# LORD JESUS CHRIST

COMES MARY     6 7 7 11.         Norman Warren (b. 1934)

1 Comes Mary to the grave:
   no singing bird has spoken,
   nor has the world awoken.
   And in her grief all love lies lost
      and broken.

2 Says Jesus at her side —
   no longer Jesus dying —
   'Why, Mary, are you crying?'
   She turns, with joy, 'My Lord! my love!'
      replying.

3 With Mary on this day
   we join our voices praising
   the God of Jesus' raising,
   and sing the triumph of his love
      amazing.

MICHAEL PERRY (b. 1942)

**31**

CHRIST TRIUMPHANT    Irregular    Michael Baughen (b. 1930)

**With triumphant vigour**

# TRIUMPHANT IN GLORY

1 Christ triumphant, ever reigning
  Saviour, Master, King,
  Lord of heav'n, our lives sustaining,
  Hear us as we sing.
  Yours the glory and the crown —
  The high renown —
  The eternal name.

2 Word incarnate, truth revealing,
  Son of Man on earth,
  Power and majesty concealing
  By your humble birth.
  Yours the glory and the crown—
  The high renown—
  The eternal name.

3 Suffering servant, scorned, ill-treated,
  Victim crucified,
  Death is through the cross defeated
  Sinners justified.
  Yours the glory and the crown—
  The high renown—
  The eternal name.

4 Priestly King, enthroned for ever
  High in heaven above,
  Sin and death and hell shall never
  Stifle hymns of love.
  Yours the glory and the crown—
  The high renown—
  The eternal name.

5 So, our hearts and voices raising
  Through the ages long,
  Ceaselessly upon you gazing
  This shall be our song.
  Yours the glory and the crown—
  The high renown—
  The eternal name.

MICHAEL SAWARD (b. 1932)

**32**

COTTON WEAVER     878787

Lancashire Folk Song
*arr Robin Sheldon (b. 1932)*

*This tune can well be transposed 1 or 2 tones higher.*

*\*optional melody notes for final verse*

1 Jesus is the Lord of living,
  All creation's bright array:
  Hearts for loving and forgiving,
  Ordered round of work and play—
    Jesus is the Lord of living,
    Year by year and day by day.

2 Jesus is the Man for others,
  Love of God in man made plain:
  Those whom God created brothers
  Now in Christ are one again—
    Jesus is the Man for others,
    Ours the pardon, his the pain.

3 Jesus is the Prince of glory,
  Love and praise to him be shown:
  Love for our salvation's story,
  Praise for his eternal throne—
    Jesus is the Prince of glory,
    Glory be to him alone.

TIMOTHY DUDLEY-SMITH (b. 1926)

# 33

**GRAFTON** 87.87.87.

French Church Melody from
'Chants Ordinaires de l'Office Divin' Paris 1881
*Harmonized by Sidney Nicholson (1875 — 1947)*

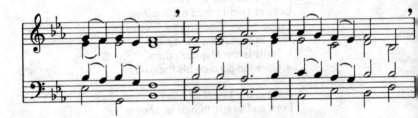

1 Who is Jesus? Friend of sinners,
  Whom in love the Father gave;
  Born within a borrowed stable,
  Laid within a borrowed grave.
  Son of God and son of Mary,
  Sons of men to seek and save.

2 Who is Jesus? Man of sorrows!
  See his glory all put by.
  Prince of life and sinners' ransom
  Stumbles forth to bleed and die.
  Lamb of God and Love immortal
  Hangs upon the cross on high.

3 Who is Jesus? Risen Saviour!
  To his Father's throne restored.
  Firstborn of the new creation,
  Sun and star and saints' reward —
  Prince of glory, King of ages,
  Christ the ever-living Lord!

TIMOTHY DUDLEY-SMITH (b. 1926)

# 34

**JESUS IS LORD** 11.12.11.12. and Refrain David J. Mansell

*With majesty*

## TRIUMPHANT IN GLORY

1 Jesus is Lord! Creation's voice proclaims it,
  For by his power each tree and flower was planned and
                                                    made.
  Jesus is Lord! the universe declares it.
  Sun, moon and stars in heaven cry Jesus is Lord!

  *Jesus is Lord! Jesus is Lord!*
  *Praise him with 'Hallelujahs' for Jesus is Lord!*

2 Jesus is Lord! yet from his throne eternal
  In flesh he came to die in pain on Calv'ry's tree.
  Jesus is Lord! from him all life proceeding,
  Yet gave his life a ransom, thus setting us free.
    *Refrain*

3 Jesus is Lord! o'er sin the mighty conqueror,
  From death he rose and all his foes shall own his name.
  Jesus is Lord! God sends his Holy Spirit
  To show by works of power that Jesus is Lord.
    *Refrain*

DAVID MANSELL

**35**

CROSS OF JESUS        87.87.        John Stainer (1840−1901)
from 'The Crucifixion' 1887

MAY HILL        87.87.        Sydney Watson (b. 1903)

## HIS NATURE

1 For your gift of God the Spirit,
   Power to make our lives anew,
   Pledge of life and hope of glory,
   Saviour, we would worship you.

2 He who in creation's dawning
   Brooded o'er the pathless deep,
   Still across our nature's darkness
   Moves to wake our souls from sleep.

3 He himself, the living author,
   Wakes to life the sacred word;
   Reads with us its holy pages,
   And reveals our risen Lord.

4 He it is who works within us,
   Teaching rebel hearts to pray;
   He whose holy intercessions
   Rise for us both night and day.

5 He, the mighty God, indwells us:
   His to strengthen, help, empower;
   His to overcome the tempter —
   Ours to call in danger's hour.

6 In his strength we dare to battle
   All the raging hosts of sin,
   And by him alone we conquer
   Foes without and foes within.

7 Fill us with your holy fullness,
   God the Father, Spirit, Son;
   In us, through us, then, forever,
   Shall your perfect will be done.

MARGARET CLARKSON (b. 1915)

**36**

SKYE BOAT SONG     CM and Refrain     Scottish Folk Song
*arr. Alastair Durden (b. 1948)*

# HIS NATURE

*Spirit of God, unseen as the wind,*
*Gentle as is the dove;*
*Teach us the truth and help us believe,*
*Show us the Saviour's love.*

1 You spoke to men long, long ago,
  Gave us the written Word;
  We read it still, needing its truth,
  Through it God's voice is heard.
    *Chorus*

2 Without Your help we fail our Lord,
  We cannot live His way;
  We need Your power, we need Your strength,
  Following Christ each day.
    *Chorus*

MARGARET OLD (b. 1932)

**37**

DAY OF THE SPIRIT          66.65.D          John Maynard

*Unison with a swing*

1. We went with a mes - sage and forced them to

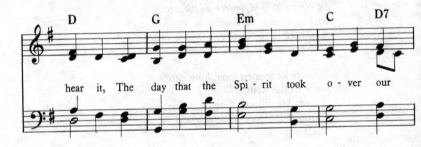

hear it, The day that the Spi - rit took o - ver our

*Fine*

lives. [*instrumental link* — — — — — — — ]

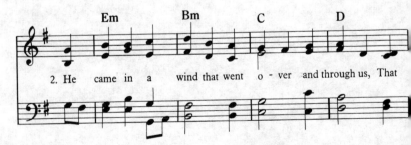

2. He came in a wind that went o - ver and through us, That

## PENTECOST—WHITSUN

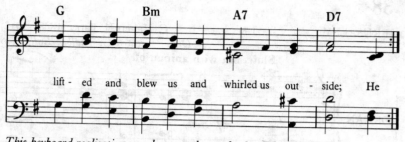

lift - ed and blew us and whirled us out - side; He

*This keyboard realisation may be treated very freely—Ed.*

1 We went with a message
   And forced them to hear it,
   The day that the Spirit
   Took over our lives.

2 He came in a wind that
   Went over and through us,
   That lifted and blew us
   And whirled us outside;
   He set us on fire and
   We had to declare it,
   The day that the Spirit
   Came down as our Guide.

3 He filled us with courage
   That nothing could smother.
   They looked at each other
   And blamed it on wine.
   But that was a sneer we
   Did nothing to merit
   The day that the Spirit
   Performed his design.

4 They shouted us down and
   They put us in prison,
   But still had to listen
   And not shut their ears.
   As Jesus had said, we
   Were able to bear it
   The day that the Spirit
   Disposed of our fears.

5 And why are we talking,
   Who live in the present,
   As if we were present
   That famous Third Hour?
   Why, we are their brothers,
   Entitled to share it —
   The day that the Spirit
   Exploded in power.

MICHAEL HEWLETT

**38**

JERUSALEM          D.L.M.          C. Hubert H. Parry (1848–1918)
*Organ part arr. G. Thalben-Ball, 1946*

**Slow, but with animation**

ORGAN

*Verse 1*

# HIS RENEWING POWER

# HOLY SPIRIT

## HIS RENEWING POWER

# HOLY SPIRIT

## HIS RENEWING POWER

1 Lord may we see your hands and side
   Touch you and feel your presence near
   Lord could our eyes behold those clouds
   And watch you rising disappear.
   Help us to pray for your return
   To watch until you come to reign
   And be your witnesses through the world
   To speak and glorify your name.

2 Lord unto you we lift our eyes
   Help us to live as you desire
   Bring down upon us power to win
   Through tongues of Holy Spirit fire.
   Lord breathe upon us to receive
   The grace and love your Spirit gives
   And may we know you with us now
   Because in us your Spirit lives.

CHRISTOPHER PORTEOUS (b. 1935)

**39**

SOUND OF WIND 66.86.66. Robin Sheldon (b. 1932

## HIS RENEWING POWER

1 When God the Spirit came
  Upon his church outpoured
  In sound of wind and sign of flame
  They spread his truth abroad,
  And filled with the Spirit
  Proclaimed that Christ is Lord.

2 What courage, power and grace
  That youthful church displayed!
  To men of every tribe and race
  They witnessed unafraid,
  And filled with the Spirit
  They broke their bread and prayed.

3 They saw God's Word prevail,
  His kingdom still increase,
  No part of all his purpose fail,
  No promised blessing cease,
  And filled with the Spirit
  Knew love and joy and peace.

4 Their theme was Christ alone,
  The Lord who lived and died,
  Who rose to his eternal throne
  At God the Father's side;
  And filled with the Spirit
  The church was multiplied.

5 So to this present hour
  Our task is still the same,
  In pentecostal love and power
  His gospel to proclaim,
  And filled with the Spirit,
  Rejoice in Jesus' Name.

TIMOTHY DUDLEY-SMITH (b. 1926)

# 40

WHITSUN PSALM          L.M.                    Noel Tredinnick

SECOND TUNE                    William Gardiner'
                                        'Sacred Melodies' London 181:
FULDA          L.M.

## HIS RENEWING POWER

1 Born by the Holy Spirit's breath,
  Loosed from the law of sin and death,
  Now cleared in Christ from every claim
  No judgement stands against our name.

2 In us the Spirit makes his home
  That we in him may overcome;|
  Christ's risen life, in all its powers,
  Its all-prevailing strength, is ours.

3 Sons, then, and heirs of God most high,
  We by his Spirit 'Father' cry;
  That Spirit with our spirit shares
  To frame and breathe our wordless prayers.

4 One is his love, his purpose one;
  To form the likeness of his Son
  In all who, called and justified,
  Shall reign in glory at his side.

5 Nor death nor life, nor powers unseen,
  Nor height nor depth can come between;
  We know through peril, pain and sword,
  The love of God in Christ our Lord.

TIMOTHY DUDLEY-SMITH (b. 1926)

# 41

REJOICE AND BE GLAD      Irregular      Priscilla Wright

## HIS RENEWING POWER

*Fear not, rejoice and be glad, the Lord hath*
   *done a great thing;*
*Hath poured out his Spirit on all mankind,*
   *on those who confess his Name.*

1 The fig tree is budding, the vine beareth fruit,
   The wheat fields are golden with grain.
   Thrust in the sickle, the harvest is ripe,
   The Lord has given us rain.
      *Refrain*

2 Ye shall eat in plenty and be satisfied,
   The mountains will drip with sweet wine.
   My children shall drink of the fountain of life,
   My children will know they are mine.
      *Refrain*

3 My people shall know that I am the Lord,
   Their shame I have taken away.
   My Spirit will lead them together again,
   My Spirit will show them the way.
      *Refrain*

4 My children shall dwell in a body of love,
   A light to the world they will be.
   Life shall come forth from the Father above,
   My body will set mankind free.
      *Refrain*

**CELEBRATION SERVICES INTERNATIONAL**

## 42

STRENGTH AND STAY     11.10.11.10.      J. B. Dykes (1823—187 ̶

## HIS RENEWING POWER

1 Indwelling Power, the promise of the Master,
  Transform our lives and make our hearts your own,
  With you as Guide, our feet may follow faster,
  Surer our step, when we are not alone.

2 Clearer the Way, as you interpret for us,
  Shedding new light upon God's Holy Word;
  Above the noise of this world's clamorous chorus
  Your 'still small voice' can be distinctly heard:

3 Voice of assurance! Voice, too, of conviction,
  Making us conscious of the stain of sin —
  We need your cleansing, and your benediction,
  Before we know a sense of peace within.

4 If courage fails, when called upon to witness,
  Bring to our minds our Master's words and deeds:
  We do not have to trust in human fitness —
  Your prompting power provides for all our needs.

5 When dark days come, or overwhelming sorrow,
  We turn to you, strong Comforter and Friend,
  To lead us through the stress towards a morrow
  Calm with a radiance that shall never end.

6 We celebrate your coming, with thanksgiving,
  At that first Pentecost so long ago,
  And, in these days, with power for present living,
  Which, mighty Spirit, you on us bestow.

EILEEN ABBOTT (b. 1912)

# THE TRINITY

**43**

## BARBARA ALLEN

8 7 8 7

English Folk melody
arr. by Robin Sheldon (b. 1932)

1 My Lord of light who made the worlds,
  in wisdom you have spoken;
  but those who heard your wise commands
  your holy law have broken.

2 My Lord of love who knew no sin,
  a sinner's death enduring,
  for us you wore a crown of thorns,
  a crown of life securing.

3 My Lord of life who came in fire
  when Christ was high ascended,
  your burning love is now released,
  our days of fear are ended.

4 My Lord of lords, one Trinity,
  to your pure name be given
  all glory now and evermore,
  all praise in earth and heaven.

CHRISTOPHER IDLE (b. 1938)

**44**

CROSS OF JESUS      8 7 8 7      John Stainer (1840—1901)
*From 'The Crucifixion' 1887*

1 Praise the Father, God of justice;
   sinners tremble at his voice,
   crowns and creatures fall before him,
   saints triumphantly rejoice.

2 Praise the Son, who comes with burning,
   purging sin and healing pain,
   by whose cross and resurrection
   we may die to rise again.

3 Praise the Spirit; power and wisdom,
   peace that like a river flows,
   word of Christ and consolation,
   life by whom his body grows.

4 Praise the Father, Son and Spirit,
   one in three and three in one,
   God our judge and God our saviour,
   God our heaven on earth begun!

MICHAEL PERRY (b. 1942)

**45**

LET US PRAISE      Irregular

Calhoun melody
*arr. David Wilson (b. 1940)*

# WORSHIP AND PRAISE

1 Let us praise God together,
Let us praise.
Let us praise God together,
All our days.
He is faithful in all his ways,
He is worthy of all our praise,
His name be exalted on high.

2 Let us seek God together,
Let us pray,
Let us seek his forgiveness,
As we pray.
He will cleanse us from all our sin,
He will help us the fight to win,
His name be exalted on high.

3 Let us serve God together,
Him obey;
Let our lives show his goodness
Through each day;
Christ the Lord is the world's true light,
Let us serve him with all our might;
His name be exalted on high.

J. E. SEDDON (b. 1915)

BATTLE HYMN  14.14.14.6 and refrain  Traditional Air
*arr. Robin Sheldon (b. 1932)*

*Chorus*

# WORSHIP AND PRAISE

1 Our eyes have seen the glory of our Saviour, Christ the Lord;
  He's seated at his Father's side in love and full accord;
  From there upon the sons of men his Spirit is out-poured,
  All hail, ascended King!
    *Glory, glory, Hallelujah,*
    *Glory, glory, Hallelujah,*
    *Glory, glory, Hallelujah,*
    *All hail, ascended King!*

2 He came to earth at Christmas and was made a man like us;
  He taught, he healed, he suffered — and they nailed him to a cross;
  He rose again on Easter Day — our Lord victorious,
  All hail, ascended King!
    *Chorus*

3 The good news of his Kingdom must be preached to every shore,
  The news of peace and pardon, and the end of strife and war;
  The secret of his Kingdom is to serve him evermore,
  All hail, ascended King!
    *Chorus*

4 His Kingdom is a family of men of every race,
  They live their lives in harmony, enabled by his grace;
  They follow his example till they see him face to face,
  All hail, ascended King!
    *Chorus*

*5 We thank him for the blessings which are yours and which are mine,
  We thank him for the lives and loves which in the darkness shine,
  We thank him in our fellowship and share the bread and wine,
  All hail, ascended King!
    *Chorus*

6 To Jesus be the glory and the vict'ry and the crown;
  When he'd ascended up to heav'n, he sent his Spirit down;
  We ask that he may guide and guard our country and our town,
  All hail, ascended King!
    *Chorus*

7 And now we bring ourselves to him, because we love him most;
  We join our hymns and shouts of praise with all the heavenly host;
  To God the Father, God the Son and God the Holy Ghost,
  All hail, ascended King!
    *Chorus*

ROLAND MEREDITH (b. 1932)

*can be omitted*

# THE CHURCH

## 47

Don Fishel (b. 1928)
arr. *Betty Pulkingham*

**ALLELUIA**     8 8 and refrain

*Capo 3 (D)*

*Alleluia, alleluia, give thanks to the risen Lord,*
*Alleluia, alleluia, give praise to his Name.*

1 Jesus is Lord of all the earth.
   He is the King of creation.
     *Refrain*

2 Spread the good news o'er all the earth.
   Jesus has died and risen.
     *Refrain*

3 We have been crucified with Christ.
   Now we shall live for ever.
     *Refrain*

4 Come let us praise the living God,
   Joyfully sing to our Saviour.
     *Refrain*

# 48

**HOLY, HOLY**     8 12.15.8.     Jimmy Owens

*melody below*

(Unison) 1 Ho-ly,   ho - ly,    ho - ly,

ho - ly.    Ho-ly, ho - ly,_____ Lord God Al -

# THE CHURCH

migh - ty; And we lift our hearts be-fore you as a

tok - en of our love, Ho - ly, ho - ly, ho - ly,

ho - ly. 2 Gra - cious -lu - jah.

# THE CHURCH

*Any of the following may be sung in parts*

1 Holy, holy, holy, holy,
   Holy, holy, Lord God Almighty;
   And we lift our hearts before you as a token of our love,
   Holy, holy, holy, holy.

2 Gracious Father, gracious Father,
   We're so glad to be your children, gracious Father;
   And we lift our heads before you as a token of our love,
   Gracious Father, gracious Father.

3 Precious Jesus, precious Jesus,
   We're so glad that you've redeemed us, precious Jesus,
   And we lift our hands before you as a token of our love,
   Precious Jesus, precious Jesus.

4 Holy Spirit, Holy Spirit,
   Come and fill our hearts anew, Holy Spirit,
   And we lift our voice before you as a token of our love.
   Holy Spirit, Holy Spirit.

5 Holy, holy, *(same as verse 1)*

6 Hallelujah, hallelujah, hallelujah, hallelujah,
   And we lift our hearts before you as a token of our love,
   Hallelujah, hallelujah.

# WORSHIP AND PRAISE

### alternative version for organ

**HOLY, HOLY**

arr. Robin Sheldon (b. 1932)

**49**

THOU ART WORTHY      Irregular          Pauline Mills

## WORSHIP AND PRAISE

1 Thou art worthy, thou art worthy,
Thou art worthy, O Lord.
Thou art worthy, to receive glory,
Glory and honour and power.
For thou hast created, hast all things created,
For thou hast created all things.
And for thy pleasure they are created;
Thou art worthy, O Lord.

2 Thou art worthy, thou art worthy,
Thou art worthy, O Lamb.
Thou art worthy, to receive glory.
And power at the Father's right hand.
For thou hast redeemed us, hast ransomed and cleaned us
By thy blood setting us free.
In white robes arrayed us, kings and priests made us,
And we are reigning in thee.

TOM SMAIL

# 50

PRAISE THE LORD 11.10.11.9. Leslie Osborne

1 Praise the Lord in the rhythm of your music,
  Praise the Lord in the freedom of your dance,
  Praise the Lord in the church and in the city,
  Praise him in the living of your life!

2 Praise the Lord on the organ and the piano,
  Praise the Lord on guitar and on the drums,
  Praise the Lord on the tambourine and cymbals,
  Praise him in the singing of your song!

3 Praise the Lord with the movement of your bodies,
  Praise the Lord with the clapping of your hands,
  Praise the Lord with your poetry and painting,
  Praise him in the acting of your play!

4 Praise the Lord in the feeding of the hungry,
  Praise the Lord in the healing of disease,
  Praise the Lord as you show his love in action,
  Praise him in your caring for the poor!

5 Praise the Lord every nation, every people,
  Praise the Lord men and women, old and young,
  Praise the Lord, let us celebrate together,
  Praise him everything in heaven and earth!

PETER CASEY (b. 1948)

# 51

SERVANTS OF GOD      10.10.11.11.      Patrick Appleford (b. 1924)

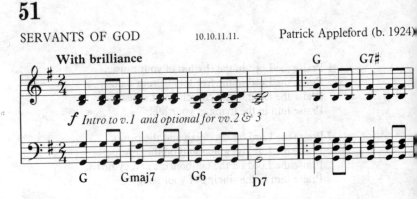

*f Intro to v.1 and optional for vv.2 & 3*

*add to last verse only*

## WORSHIP AND PRAISE

A - men.

1 Servants of God, the Almighty, the Lord,
Worshipping, praising and hearing your word,
Prayer and thanksgiving we offer before you,
Here in this temple we humbly adore you.

2 Servants of Christ, the redeemer of all,
Here we are met in response to your call,
Using your talents in praising and singing,
Each one his gifts to the Saviour is bringing —

3 Servants of God, the great Spirit of power,
Giving us guidance and strength every hour,
Come as you came to th'apostles of old,
Come Holy Spirit and make us more bold — to
Live every minute as servants of God
Praising for ever our glorious Lord. Amen.

JOHN GLANDFIELD

**52**

HIS HOUSE  764D.7666  *arr. Robin Sheldon (b. 1932)*

**Slowly**

*Intro to v. 1* - - - - - - - - - - - - - - - -

*Verses*

1 We are come into his house
   And gathered in his name
   To worship him *(repeat first 3 lines)*

   We are come into his house
   And gathered in his name
   To worship Christ the Lord.
   Worship him, Christ the Lord.

2 Let's forget about ourselves
   And concentrate on him
   And worship him *(repeat first 3 lines)*

   Let's forget about ourselves
   And concentrate on him
   And worship Christ the Lord.
   Worship him, Christ the Lord.

3 He is all my righteousness
   I stand complete in him
   And worship him *(repeat first 3 lines)*

   He is all my righteousness
   I stand complete in him
   And worship Christ the Lord.
   Worship him, Christ the Lord.

4 So let's lift up holy hands
   And magnify his name
   And worship him *(repeat first 3 lines)*

   So let's lift up holy hands
   And magnify his name
   And worship Christ the Lord.
   Worship him, Christ the Lord.

BRUCE BALLINGER

**53**

MO RANCH    6 6 6 6 D    Erik Routley (b. 1917)

Al - le - lu - ia,

## WORSHIP AND PRAISE

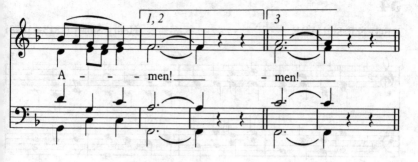

1 Come, Christians, join to sing
  Alleluia, Amen!
  loud praise to Christ our King,
  Alleluia, Amen!
  Let all with heart and voice
  before his throne rejoice;
  praise is his gracious choice.
  Alleluia, Amen!

2 Come lift your hearts on high
  Alleluia, Amen!
  let praises fill the sky,
  Alleluia, Amen!
  He is our guide and friend;
  to us he'll condescend;
  his love shall never end.
  Alleluia, Amen!

3 Praise yet your Christ again,
  Alleluia, Amen!
  Life shall not end the strain
  Alleluia, Amen!
  On heaven's blissful shore
  his goodness we'll adore,
  singing for evermore,
  Alleluia, Amen!

C. E. BATEMAN

*This hymn was composed in July 1973 at Mo Ranch, Texas for the Presbyterian Musicians' Convention.*

**54**

REGENT SQUARE          8 7 8 7 8 7          Henry Smart (1813—1879)

# WORSHIP AND PRAISE

1 Praise the Lord, sing hallelujah!
Children of God's gracious choice;
Let his praises rise as thunder,
Let the whole earth hear his voice;
Till the song of his salvation
Makes his broken world rejoice!

2 Man's imprisoning night is shattered
At the impact of his Word;
Light and life spring forth eternal
Where that mighty voice is heard;
Let the powers of death and darkness
Own the triumph of their Lord!

3 Praise the Lord until his glory
Floods the farthest realms of earth,
Till from every tribe and nation
Souls rise up in glad rebirth;
Haste the day of his appearing
When all creatures own his worth.

4 Praise the Lord, sing hallelujah!
Sound his sovereign grace abroad,
Till his Word is loved and honoured
Everywhere man's feet have trod;
Till his ransomed family gathers
Safely round the throne of God!

MARGARET CLARKSON (b. 1915)

**55**
THANK YOU, LORD
*Capo 2 (C)*

Irregular

Ed Baggett
*arr. Betty Pulkingham*

here on    earth    of which  we  sing and  share.
sets us    free     to serve  you with our  lives.

king!

*We really want to thank you, Lord.*
*We really want to bless your name.*
*Halleluia, Jesus is our king!*
*Halleluia, Jesus is our king!*

1 We thank you, Lord, for your gift to us,
   your life so rich beyond compare,
The gift of your body here on earth
   of which we sing and share.
   *Refrain*

2 We thank you, Lord, for our life together,
   to live and move in the love of Christ,
Tenderness which sets us free
   to serve you with our lives.
   *Refrain*

THE 'FISHERMEN'

*See also Nos. 127, 128, 129 from the section 'God in the Psalms'*

**56**

Melody by Hans Hassler (1564—1612)
*Adapted and harmonised by*
*J. S. Bach (1685—1750)*

PASSION CHORALE      7 6 7 6 D

1  We come as guests invited
   When Jesus bids us dine,
   His friends on earth united
   To share the bread and wine;
   The bread of life is broken,
   The wine is freely poured
   For us, in solemn token
   Of Christ our dying Lord.

2  We eat and drink, receiving
   From Christ the grace we need,
   And in our hearts believing
   On Him by faith we feed;
   With wonder and thanksgiving
   For love that knows no end,
   We find in Jesus living
   Our ever-present Friend.

3  One Bread is ours for sharing,
   One single fruitful Vine,
   Our fellowship declaring
   Renewed in bread and wine—
   Renewed, sustained, and given
   By token, sign and word,
   The pledge and seal of heaven,
   The love of Christ our Lord.

TIMOTHY DUDLEY-SMITH (b. 1926)

PLATTS LANE     5 6 6 4     Evelyn Sharpe (1884–1969)
and compilers

From *Enlarged Songs of Praise* by permission of
Oxford University Press (altered by permission)

## HOLY COMMUNION

1 As we break the bread
and taste the life of wine,
we bring to mind our Lord,
man of all time.

2 Grain is sown to die;
it rises from the dead,
becomes through human toil
our common bread.

3 Pass from hand to hand
the living love of Christ!
Machine and man provide
bread for this feast.

4 Jesus binds in one
our daily life and work;
he is of all mankind
symbol and mark.

5 Having shared the bread
that died to rise again,
we rise to serve the world,
scattered as grain.

FRED KAAN (b. 1929)

SELFLESS LOVE    14.14.14.14.    Andrew Maries

*Slow and tender*

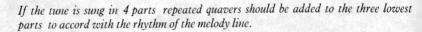

*If the tune is sung in 4 parts repeated quavers should be added to the three lowest parts to accord with the rhythm of the melody line.*

## HOLY COMMUNION

1 He gave his life in selfless love, for sinful men he came,
  He had no guilt or sin himself but suffered for our blame,
  He took the cup of pain and death, his blood was freely shed,
  We see his body on the cross, we share his living bread.

2 He did not die to call the good but sinners to repent.
  It was the lame, the deaf, the blind for whom his life was spent.
  To heal the sick, to find the lost—it was for such he came
  And round your table Lord, we come, to praise your holy name.

3 We heard him call his Father's name, 'Tis finished' was his cry.
  We also have forsaken him and left him there to die.
  The sins which crucified our Lord are sins his blood has cured,
  And death could not defeat the love his perfect life ensured.

4 His body, broken there for us, has risen now above,
  The cup of blessing we receive, a sharing of his love.
  Partaking of the living bread his death we shall proclaim
  Until the hour which surely nears when Jesus comes again.

CHRISTOPHER PORTEOUS (b. 1935)

**59**

LIVING LORD        Irregular

Patrick Appleford (b. 1924)

vvs. 1 & 3    Link - - - - -    2 & 4

# HOLY COMMUNION

1 Lord Jesus Christ,
  You have come to us,
  You are one with us,
  Mary's Son.
  Cleansing our souls from all their sin,
  Pouring your love and goodness in,
  Jesus our love for you we sing,
  Living Lord.

2 Lord Jesus Christ,
  Now and every day,
  Teach us how to pray,
  Son of God.
  You have commanded us to do
  This in remembrance, Lord, of you;
  Into our lives your power breaks through,
  Living Lord.

3 Lord Jesus Christ,
  You have come to us,
  Born as one of us,
  Mary's Son.
  Led out to die on Calvary,
  Risen from death to set us free,
  Living Lord Jesus, help us see
  You are Lord.

4 Lord Jesus Christ,
  I would come to you,
  Live my life for you,
  Son of God.
  All your commands I know are true,
  Your many gifts will make me new,
  Into my life your power breaks through,
  Living Lord.

PATRICK APPLEFORD (b. 1924)

**60**

FRANCONIA    S.M.    W. H. Havergal (1793—1870), adapted, from a tune in Konig's *Harmonischer Liederschatz (1738)* (harmony slightly altered)

1 Father of all, with praise
  And thanks to you we come,
  For though our sins had driven us far
  Your love has brought us home.

2 Your Son has given us grace
  And changed our sorry state;
  His death and life provide the key
  To open glory's gate.

3 This bread and wine we share:
  Christ's body we receive,
  We drink his cup and humbly seek
  His risen life to live.

4 May Christ's own Spirit flood
  The darkened world with light
  And keep us strong in Christian hope
  And make our witness bright.

5 So shall the earth be free —
  The earth to which Christ came —
  And all your children join to bless
  Your great and holy Name.

DAVID MOWBRAY (b. 1938)

SOLOTHURN    L.M.

Swiss Traditional melody

1 Now let us from this table rise
   renewed in body, mind and soul;
   with Christ we die and live again,
   his selfless love has made us whole.

2 With minds alert, upheld by grace,
   to spread the Word in speech and deed,
   we follow the steps of Christ,
   at one with man in hope and need.

3 To fill each human house with love,
   it is the sacrament of care;
   the work that Christ began to do
   we humbly pledge ourselves to share.

4 Then grant us courage, father God,
   to choose again the pilgrim way,
   and help us to accept with joy
   the challenge of tomorrow's day.

FRED KAAN (b. 1929)

# 62

**LONDONDERRY AIR**  11.10.11.10.D  Irish Traditional Melody
*arr. Robin Sheldon (b. 1932)*

### RENEWAL

1 Lord of the church, we pray for our renewing:
  Christ over all, our undivided aim.
  Fire of the Spirit, burn for our enduing,
  Wind of the Spirit, fan the living flame!
  We turn to Christ amid our fear and failing,
  The will that lacks the courage to be free,
  The weary labours, all but unavailing,
  To bring us nearer what a church should be.

2 Lord of the church, we seek a Father's blessing,
  A true repentance and a faith restored,
  A swift obedience and a new possessing,
  Filled with the Holy Spirit of the Lord!
  We turn to Christ from all our restless striving,
  Unnumbered voices with a single prayer —
  The living water for our souls' reviving,
  In Christ to live, and love and serve and care.

3 Lord of the church, we long for our uniting,
  True to one calling, by one vision stirred;
  One cross proclaiming and one creed reciting,
  One in the truth of Jesus and his word!
  So lead us on; till toil and trouble ended,
  One church triumphant one new song shall
        sing,
  To praise his glory, risen and ascended,
  Christ over all, the everlasting King!

TIMOTHY DUDLEY- SMITH (b. 1926)

# THE CHURCH

**63**

HYFRYDOL     8 7 8 7 D     Melody by R. H. Prichard (1811—1887)

## RENEWAL

1 Fire of God, titanic Spirit,
  Burn within our hearts today,
  Cleanse our sin; may we exhibit
  Holiness in every way.
  Purge the squalidness that shames us,
  Soils the body; taints the soil.
  And through Jesus Christ who claims us,
  Purify us; make us whole.

2 Wind of God, dynamic Spirit,
  Breathe upon our hearts today
  That we may your power inherit;
  Hear us, Spirit, as we pray.
  Fill the vacuum that enslaves us,
  Emptiness of heart and soul,
  And, through Jesus Christ who saves us,
  Give us life and make us whole.

3 Voice of God, prophetic Spirit,
  Speak to every heart today,
  To encourage or prohibit,
  Urging action or delay.
  Clear the vagueness which impedes us,
  Come, enlighten mind and soul.
  And, through Jesus Christ who leads us,
  Teach the truth that makes us whole.

MICHAEL SAWARD (b. 1932)

**64**

ONE IN THE SPIRIT    Irregular    Peter Scholtes (b. 1928)
*Harm: Jack Noble White (b. 1938)*

## FELLOWSHIP AND UNITY

u - ni - ty may one day be re - stored,
spread the news that God is in our land,
dig - ni - ty and save___ each man's pride,
Spir - it who___ makes___ us___ one.

**Refrain**

And they'll know we are Christ-ians by our love, by our

love, Yes, they'll know___ we are Christ-ians by our love.___

# THE CHURCH

'1 We are one in the Spirit,
  We are one in the Lord.
  We are one in the Spirit,
  We are one in the Lord,
  And we pray that all unity may one day be restored,

  *And they'll know we are Christians by our love, by our love,*
  *Yes, they'll know we are Christians by our love.*

2 We will walk with each other,
  We will walk hand in hand.
  We will walk with each other,
  We will walk hand in hand,
  And together we'll spread the news that God is in our land,
    *Chorus*

3 We will work with each other,
  We will work side by side.
  We will work with each other,
  We will work side by side,
  And we'll guard each man's dignity and save each man's pride,
    *Chorus*

4 All praise to the Father,
  From whom all things come,
  And all praise to Christ Jesus,
  His only Son,
  And all praise to the Spirit who makes us one.
    *Chorus*

PETER SCHOLTES (b. 1928)

DUKE STREET    L.M.    Late 18th-century melody
Attributed to J. Hatton (*d.* 1793)

1 Forth in the peace of Christ we go;
   Christ to the world with joy we bring;
   Christ in our minds, Christ on our lips,
   Christ in our hearts, the world's true King.

2 King of our hearts, Christ makes us kings;
   Kingship with him his servants gain;
   With Christ, the Servant-Lord of all,
   Christ's world we serve to share Christ's reign.

3 Priests of the world, Christ sends us forth
   This world of time to consecrate,
   This world of sin by grace to heal,
   Christ's world in Christ to re-create.

4 Christ's are our lips, his word we speak;
   Prophets are we whose deeds proclaim
   Christ's truth in love that we may be
   Christ in the world, to spread Christ's name.

5 We are the Church; Christ bids us show
   That in his Church all nations find
   Their hearth and home where Christ restores
   True peace, true love, to all mankind.

JAMES QUINN (b. 1919)

By permission of Geoffrey Chapman, Publishers
Alternative tune – Angel's Song (Song 34)
AMR–336, AHB–294

**66**

FULDA      L.M.      William Gardiner, *Sacred Melodies, 1815*

## OUTREACH

1 We have a gospel to proclaim,
   good news for men in all the earth;
   the gospel of a Saviour's name:
   we sing his glory, tell his worth.

2 Tell of his birth at Bethlehem
   not in a royal house or hall
   But in a stable dark and dim,
   the Word made flesh, a light for all.

3 Tell of his death at Calvary,
   hated by those he came to save,
   in lonely suffering on the Cross;
   for all he loved his life he gave.

4 Tell of that glorious Easter morn:
   empty the tomb, for he was free.
   he broke the power of death and hell
   that we might share his victory.

5 Tell of his reign at God's right hand,
   by all creation glorified.
   He sends his Spirit on his Church
   to live for him, the Lamb who died.

6 Now we rejoice to name him King:
   Jesus is Lord of all the earth.
   This gospel-message we proclaim:
   we sing his glory, tell his worth.

EDWARD J. BURNS (b. 1938)

# 67

WANSBECK     11.11.11.5     Erik Routley (b. 1917)

## OUTREACH

1 Lord, as we rise to leave this shell of worship,
  Called to the risk of unprotected living.
  Willing to be at one with all your people.
  We ask for courage.

2 For all the strain with living interwoven.
  For the demands each day will make upon us,
  And for the love we owe the modern city.
  Lord, make us cheerful.

3 Give us an eye for opening to serve you:
  Make us alert when calm is interrupted,
  Ready and wise to use the unexpected:
  Sharpen our insight.

4 Lift from our life the blanket of convention:
  Give us the nerve to lose our life to others.
  Be with your church in death and resurrection,
  Lord of all ages!

FRED KAAN (b. 1929)

**68**

SUTTON TRINITY  6 5 6 5 D  F. Pratt Green (b. 1903)

# OUTREACH

1 When the Church of Jesus
   Shuts its outer door,
   Lest the roar of traffic
   Drown the voice of prayer:
   May our prayers, Lord, make us
   Ten times more aware
   That the world we banish
   Is our Christian care.

2 If our hearts are lifted
   Where devotion soars
   High above this hungry
   Suffering world of ours:
   Lest our hymns should drug us
   To forget its needs,
   Forge our Christian worship
   Into Christian deeds.

3 Lest the gifts we offer,
   Money, talents, time,
   Serve to salve our conscience
   To our secret shame:
   Lord, reprove, inspire us
   By the way you give;
   Teach us, dying Saviour,
   How true Christians live.

F. PRATT GREEN (b. 1903)

**69**

GO FORTH   10.10.10.10.   Michael Baughen (b. 1930)

**With a swing**
*Unison*

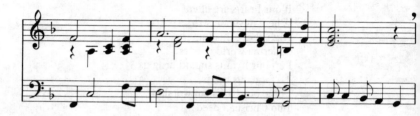

## OUTREACH

1 Go forth and tell! O Church of God, awake!
  God's saving news to all the nations take.
  Proclaim Christ Jesus, Saviour, Lord and King,
  That all the world his worthy praise may sing.

2 Go forth and tell! God's love embraces all:
  He will in grace respond to all who call.
  How shall they call if they have never heard
  The gracious invitation of his Word?

3 Go forth and tell! Men still in darkness lie:
  In wealth or want, in sin they live and die.
  Give us, O Lord, concern of heart and mind,
  A love like yours which cares for all mankind.

4 Go forth and tell! The doors are open wide:
  Share God's good gifts with men so long denied.
  Live out your life as Christ, your Lord, shall choose,
  Your ransomed powers for his sole glory use.

5 Go forth and tell! O Church of God, arise:
  Go in the strength which Christ your Lord supplies.
  Go, till all nations his great name adore
  And serve him Lord and King for evermore.

J. E. SEDDON (b. 1915)

# THE CHURCH

## 70

**CAPITOL HEIGHTS**      8 7 8 7 D            Beryl Vick, Jr.

## OUTREACH

1 In this age of noise and turmoil
   Change and doubts confuse each life;
   Paces quicken, peace eludes us,
   All our days are filled with strife.
   Thoughts once held and hopes once cherished
   Crumble in a modern light,
   But the truth as taught by Jesus
   Stands to guide us to the right.

2 Now awake, O Church, and teach us
   Truths once taught at Galilee;
   Train us for the tasks before us,
   Train us for eternity.
   Make us strong and give us courage,
   Teach us methods for this day,
   Let the message taught by Jesus
   Clearly lead us on our way.

3 Let us not grow tired of learning,
   What we learn can make us free;
   Let us do the work before us,
   Let us live abundantly!
   Learning, teaching, striving, winning,
   Living, so that all can see
   That the life shown us by Jesus
   Ever shall our pattern be.

BETH LUTTRELL

# 71

LORD OF THE YEARS        11.10.11.10.        Michael Baughen
*arr. Robin Sheldon (b. 1932)*

## OUTREACH

1 Lord, we have come, our need and guilt confessing:
   Our souls are fed but others hunger still.
   We all, in selfish ease your love possessing,
   Have tried, but failed, your purpose to fulfil.

2 Help us to break the chains of our own making;
   Open our eyes new paths ahead to see,
   Sure of the changeless message we are taking,
   Proud to proclaim its power to set men free.

3 Give us, O Lord, a love that is unbounded,
   That reaches out to every class and race.
   Forgive us when, by prejudice surrounded,
   We set a limit to your sovereign grace.

4 Show us the need for sacrificial living,
   The Cross our pattern, inspiration, all:
   For those in need, our service gladly giving,
   Ready for swift obedience to your call.

5 Revive us, Lord, your Spirit's power impelling
   Our lives to demonstrate your truth revealed:
   Your Word upon our lips the Good News telling;
   Your peace within our hearts our strength and shield.

6 So send us forth, still your great love possessing,
   But with new vision of your saving power.
   Your Church a channel for a mighty blessing;
   This is your purpose, this the time, the hour.

J. H. CANSDALE (b. 1904)

*The version more suited to the piano can be found at No. 80*

# 72

**CHARITY**   7 7 7 5                John Stainer (1840—1901)

*Based on 'Come unto me all ye that travail' (Matthew 11. 28)*

1 Christ is all the world's Good News;
  Christ still calls the world to choose:
  Heaven to find and hell to lose,
  Turn and come to him.

2 Love into this world was sent;
  Love's full measure here was spent;
  Love to death and burial went;
  Look, and come to him.

3 Come, but counting first the cost;
  Come to bury every boast;
  Come to one who loves the lost;
  Think, and come to him.

4 If this great desire you have,
  Self must sink into the grave;
  Lose your life, and Christ will save;
  Die, and come to him.

5 But unless God draws men on
  None can come to know his Son;
  Yet his love refuses none:
  All may come to him.

6 Christ makes heavy burdens light;
  Christ turns blindness into sight;
  Fills our hunger, sets us right;
  Trust, and come to him.

7 Christ the path, the light, the door;
  Come to him whose word is sure;
  Come — you need no reasons more:
  Come, O come to him!

CHRISTOPHER IDLE (b. 1938)

**73**

SLANE      10.11.11.12      Irish Traditional Melody
*harm. by Erik Routley (b. 1917)*

## OUTREACH

1 Jesus, we've prayed and we've read from your Word,
  We've looked for your guidance, proclaimed you the Lord,
  And often we've praised for your life and your deeds,
  But when have we followed to help those in need?

2 You had no fear of being seen in the home
  Of someone whose job made him scorned and alone;
  You broke social bounds to be near the despised
  Who knew best of all of their need of your life.

3 We are afraid to break free from old ways,
  Fearful of all that the others will say;
  We have not learned what it means to step out
  And live in your world as the children of light.

4 Great is our guilt, Lord, and weak are our hearts,
  But teach us to give, Lord, to love till it hurts,
  Teach us to be to each person we meet
  Your heart, your involvement, your hands and your feet.

ANGELA REITH (b. 1952)

# 74

LITTLE CORNARD        666688        Martin Shaw (1875—1958)

# MISSIONARY

1 Jesus is King of Kings!
   All power to him is given;
   Go in his name to men,
   Tell of the Lord from heaven.
   'Tis his command, we must obey
   And serve him till that glorious day.

2 Go where the needs are great,
   Bearing the word of grace;
   Aid, in the name of Christ
   People of every race.
   The sick ones heal, the hungry feed;
   For his sake help them in their need.

3 Where there is fear and hate
   Go with the word of love;
   Peace bring to those who strive,
   War and its ills remove.
   Our Saviour Christ is always near,
   His perfect love will cast out fear.

4 Wherever you may go
   Carry the word of truth;
   News that is good for all,
   Men, women, children, youth.
   On all who hear his word aright
   Our Saviour sheds eternal light.

5 Soon comes that glorious day
   When we shall see his face;
   Members of that great throng
   Taken from every race,
   Who heard the word of life on earth
   And in their Saviour found new birth.

EDWARD BURNS (b. 1938)

# 75

JULIUS      10.10.10.10.      Martin Shaw (1875—1958)

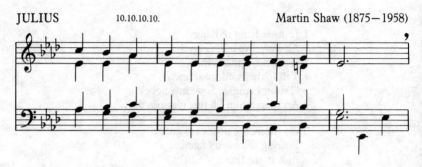

1 'Go forth!' The Lord's command rings clearly still
  Across the centuries that lie between;
  In word, in deed, in offering of the will.
  May our response to his command be seen.

2 'Go forth!' To sound abroad the word of truth,
  Ambassadors for him who died for all,
  To preach salvation and to teach the youth —
  May we who love the Lord accept his call.

3 'Go forth!' For sick and suffering need the power
  Of Christ the Healer, in far-distant lands:
  That modern skill be there in needful hour
  May we across the sea stretch loving hands.

4 'Go forth!' To take the printed word of God,
  To satisfy the hunger of the mind:
  To needs of newly literate nations, Lord,
  May we not be insensitive nor blind.

5 'Go forth!' To work with those who till the earth
  To show God's wonders in the harvest field,
  That wiser ways may prove their lasting worth,
  And in due time a fuller increase yield.

6 Send us! For all who know thee, gracious Lord,
  Who in thy boundless love and care rejoice,
  Must offer thee their lives, in deed and word,
  Must be obedient to thy voice.

EILEEN ABBOTT (b. 1912)

# 76

NEW HOPE 9 8 9 8 D Erik Routley (b. 1917)

1 The earth is the Lord's, and its fullness,  Psalm 24:1-4
 Its mystery, splendour and wealth,
 Its bounty, fertility, kindness,
 Its beauty, its reason, its health:
 Then who is the wise-hearted steward
 Who faithfully carries this trust?
 The generous, gently, obedient,
 The patient, the honest, the just.

2 The earth is the Lord's own possession,
 Not the tithe, nor the half, but the whole;
 He made it, sustains it, and leads it  Romans 8:19
 Towards its celestial goal:
 But the harmony of the Creation
 Is broken by selfhood and vice
 When the anxious, incompetent steward
 In fear keeps back part of the price.  Acts 5:2

3 The church is the Lord's, and its people
 The body of Christ, who impart
 The word and the Feast and the friendship
 (His head and his hands and his heart!)
 Where sisters and brothers together  Acts 4:32
 In worship and laughter and prayer
 Give all to each other, then heaven
 Is present on earth with them there.

4 All life is the Lord's, who in giving
 His Son gave him glory again,
 For he who surrendered his spirit  Eph. 4:9
 Is he who ascended to reign;
 So the talent when buried was withered,  Matt. 25:18
 The manna, when hoarded, decayed,  Ex. 16:20
 But love meets us in resurrection
 When love gives itself unafraid.  Mark 8:35

ERIK ROUTLEY (b. 1917)

**77**

BIRLING  L.M.

From an early 19th century MS
Adapted by Geoffrey Shaw (1879—1943)

By permission of Oxford University Press

1 The Lord made man, the Scriptures tell,
  To bear his image and his sign;
  Yet we by nature share as well
  The ancient mark of Adam's line.

2 In Adam's fall falls every man,
  With every gift the Father gave:
  The crown of all creation's plan
  Becomes a rebel and a slave.

3 Herein all woes are brought to birth,
  All aching hearts and sunless skies:
  Brightness is gone from all the earth,
  The innocence of nature dies.

4 Yet Adam's children, born to pain,
  By self enslaved, by sin enticed,
  Still may by grace be born again,
  Children of God, beloved in Christ.

5 In Christ is Adam's ransom met;
  Earth, by his cross, is holy ground;
  Eden indeed is with us yet!
  In Christ are life and freedom found!

TIMOTHY DUDLEY-SMITH (b. 1926)

ALL THROUGH THE NIGHT 7 4 8 4.8 8 4 Traditional
*arr. by Angela Reith (b. 1952)*
*and Robin Sheldon (b. 1932)*

# HARVEST

1 For the fruits of his creation
   thanks be to God;
For his gifts to every nation,
   thanks be to God;
For the ploughing, sowing, reaping,
Silent growth while men are sleeping,
Future needs in earth's safe keeping,
   thanks be to God.

2 In the just reward of labour,
   God's will is done;
In the help we give our neighbour,
   God's will is done;
In our world-wide task of caring
For the hungry and despairing,
In the harvests men are sharing,
   God's will is done.

3 For the harvests of his Spirit,
   thanks be to God;
For the good all men inherit,
   thanks be to God;
For the wonders that astound us,
For the truths that still confound us,
Most of all, that love has found us,
   thanks be to God.

F. PRATT GREEN (b. 1903)

**79**

NOW JOIN WE          9 8 9 8                    Michael Metcalf

1 Now join we, to praise the Creator,
  our voices in worship and song;
  we stand to recall with thanksgiving
  that to him all seasons belong.

## HARVEST

2 We thank you, O God, for your goodness,
  for the joy and abundance of crops,
  for food that is stored in our larders,
  for all we can buy in the shops.

3 But also of need and starvation
  we sing with concern and despair,
  of skills that are used for destruction,
  of land that is burnt and laid bare.

4 We cry for the plight of the hungry
  while harvests are left on the field,
  for orchards neglected and wasting,
  for produce from markets withheld.

5 The song grows in depth and in wideness:
  the earth and its people are one.
  There can be no thanks without giving,
  no words without deeds that are done.

6 Then teach us, O Lord of the harvest,
  to be humble in all that we claim;
  to share what we have with the nations,
  to care for the world in your name.

MICHAEL METCALF

# 80

LORD OF THE YEARS      11.10.11.10.     Michael Baughen (b. 1930) and David Wilson (b. 1940)

*The version more suited to the organ can be found at No.71*

# COMMEMORATION

1 Lord, for the years your love has kept and guided,
  Urged and inspired us, cheered us on our way;
  Sought us and saved us, pardoned and provided,
  Lord of the years, we bring our thanks today.

2 Lord, for that Word, the Word of life which fires us,
  Speaks to our hearts and sets our soul ablaze;
  Teaches and trains, rebukes us and inspires us,
  Lord of the Word, receive your people's praise.

3 Lord, for our land, in this our generation,
  Spirits oppressed by pleasure, wealth and care;
  For young and old, for commonwealth and nation,
  Lord of our land, be pleased to hear our prayer.

4 Lord, for our world, when men disown and doubt him,
  Loveless in strength and comfortless in pain;
  Hungry and helpless, lost indeed without him,
  Lord of the world, we pray that Christ may reign.

5 Lord for ourselves; in living power remake us —
  Self on the cross and Christ upon the throne —
  Past put behind us, for the future take us,
  Lord of our lives, to live for Christ alone.

TIMOTHY DUDLEY-SMITH (b. 1930)

# 81

NORTHBROOK 11.10.11.10. Reginald Thatcher (1888—1957)

From the Clarendon Hymn Book by permission of Oxford University Press

1 This is the day when light was first created,
  Symbol and gift of order and design.
  In light is God's intention clearly stated;
  The break of day reveals his loving mind.

2 This is the day of man's complete surprising,
  Repeat of Easter: Christ has come to life!
  Now is the feast of love's revolt and rising
  Against the rule of hell and death and grief.

3 We join to praise, with every race and nation,
  The God who with mankind his Spirit shares;
  Strong wind of change and earth's illumination,
  Dispelling static thoughts and darkest fears.

4 This is the day of worship and of vision,
  Great birthday of the church in every land.
  Let Christian men confess their sad division,
  And seek the strength again as one to stand.

5 We pray that this, the day of re-creation,
  May hallow all the week that is to come.
  Help us, O Lord, to lay a good foundation
  For all we do at work, at school, at home.

FRED KAAN (b. 1929)

# 82

ALL BELIEVE    8 8 8 8 Swing

Derek Hartropp
*arr. by Roger Harvey*

**With a swing and in a joyful manner** ($\textpy = 110$)

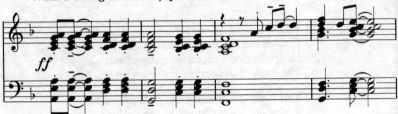

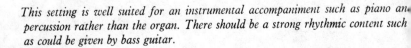

*This setting is well suited for an instrumental accompaniment such as piano and percussion rather than the organ. There should be a strong rhythmic content such as could be given by bass guitar.*

# FAITH

(for piano only)

1 Let us all believe in the Lord,
   Let us all believe in the Lord,
   Let us all believe in the Lord,
   Let us all believe in the Lord.

2 Let us all rejoice in his name,
   Let us all rejoice in his name,
   Let us all rejoice in his name,
   Let us all believe in the Lord.

3 Let us learn to love and forgive,
   Let us learn to love and forgive,
   Let us learn to love and forgive,
   Let us all believe in the Lord.

4 Let us learn the meaning of faith,
   Let us learn the meaning of faith,
   Let us learn the meaning of faith,
   Let us all believe in the Lord.

5 Let us all believe in the Lord,
   Let us all believe in the Lord,
   Let us all believe in the Lord,
   Let us all believe in the Lord.

DEREK HARTROPP

# 83

CRESSWELL      8 8 9 7 10.7      Anthony Milner (b. 1925)

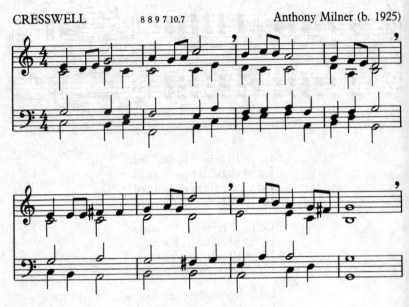

By permission Oxford University Press

1 Love is his word, love is his way,
Feasting with men, fasting alone,
Living and dying, rising again,
Love, only love, is his way.
*Richer than gold is the love of my Lord:*
*Better than splendour and wealth.*

# LOVE

2 Love is his way, love is his mark,
   Sharing his last Passover feast,
   Christ at his table, host to the twelve,
   Love, only love, is his mark.
   *Refrain*

3 Love is his mark, love is his sign,
   Bread for our strength, wine for our joy,
   'This is my body, this is my blood.'
   Love, only love, is his sign.
   *Refrain*

4 Love is his sign, love is his news,
   'Do this,' he said, 'lest you forget
   All my deep sorrow, all my dear blood.'
   Love, only love, is his news.
   *Refrain*

5 Love is his news, love is his name,
   We are his own, chosen and called,
   Family, brethren, cousins and kin.
   Love, only love, is his name.
   *Refrain*

6 Love is his name, love is his law,
   Hear his command, all who are his:
   'Love one another, I have loved you.'
   Love, only love, is his law.
   *Refrain*

7 Love is his law, love is his word:
   Love of the Lord, Father and Word,
   Love of the Spirit, God ever one.
   Love only love, is his word.
   *Refrain*

LUKE CONNAUGHTON (b. 1917)

# 84

**JONATHAN** 6 5 6 5 D Robin Sheldon (b. 1932)

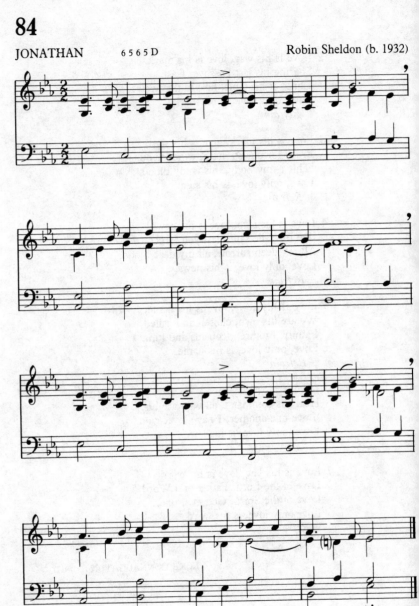

## LOVE

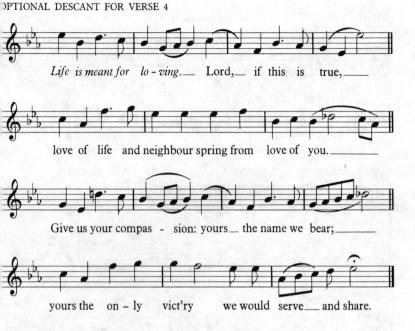

Life is meant for lo-ving.__ Lord,__ if this is true,____

love of life and neighbour spring from love of you.__

Give us your compas - sion: yours__ the name we bear;____

yours the on – ly vict'ry we would serve__ and share.

1 Life has many rhythms, every heart its beat;
   Everywhere we hear the sound of dancing feet.
   Life is this world's secret: Lord of Life, forgive,
   If we never asked you what it means to live.

2 Life is meant for loving. Lord, if this is true,
   Why do millions suffer without help from you?
   Some who fought injustice added wrong to wrong:
   Can it be that love is stronger than the strong?

3 It was you who promised: All who seek shall find.
   What we find lies deeper than our reach of mind;
   What we found was you, Lord, you the God above,
   You had come, as Victim, to the world you love!

4 Life is meant for loving. Lord, if this is true,
   Love of life and neighbour spring from love of you.
   Give us your compassion: yours the name we bear;
   Yours the only victory we would serve and share.

F. PRATT GREEN (b. 1903)

**85**

SING HOSANNA    10.8 10.9 and refrain    Traditional

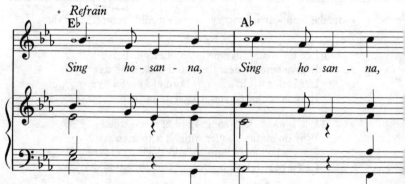

* Refrain

Sing    ho - san - na,    Sing    ho - san - na,

Sing    ho-san-na to the    king of kings!    Sing    ho-san-na,

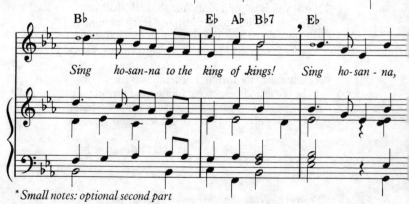

*Small notes: optional second part

# JOY

Sing, hos-an-na Sing ho-san-na to the king.

1 Give me joy in my heart, keep me praising,
  give me joy in my heart, I pray;
  give me joy in my heart, keep me praising,
  keep me praising till the break of day.
    *Sing hosanna! Sing hosanna!*
    *Sing hosanna to the king of kings!*
    *Sing hosanna! Sing hosanna!*
    *Sing hosanna to the king!*

2 Give me peace in my heart, keep me loving,
  give me peace in my heart, I pray;
  give me peace in my heart, keep me loving,
  keep me loving till the break of day.
    *Chorus*

3 Give me love in my heart, keep me serving,
  give me love in my heart, I pray;
  give me love in my heart, keep me serving,
  keep me serving till the break of day.
    *Chorus*

TRADITIONAL

REDEEMER  Irregular  Yvonne Gale (b. 1948)

1 Fa - ther I will praise___ you For
2 My heart's so full of joy_____ I

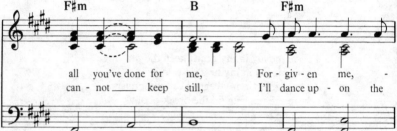

all you've done for me, For - giv - en me, -
can - not ___ keep still, I'll dance up - on the

- stored me And healed me in - ward - ly, You
fresh fields I'll jump the high - est hill For

filled me with your joy, Lord, Your ___ love so fresh and
you are my Cre - a - tor, My Re - deem - er and my

# JOY

new,      And gi-ven me a heart of praise To
friend,      You keep me by your love and grace, I'll

sing and dance to you. *For as long as I have*
praise you a-gain and a-gain.

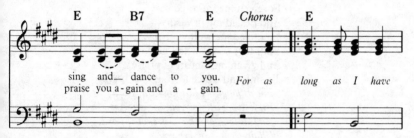

breath Lord I'll live my life for you, And as

long as I have strength, Lord, I'll dance to wor-ship

you. *For as* dance to wor-ship you.

# THE CHRISTIAN LIFE

1 Father I will praise you
　For all you've done for me,
　Forgiven me, restored me
　And healed me inwardly,
　You filled me with your joy, Lord,
　Your love so fresh and new,
　And given me a heart of praise
　To sing and dance to you.
　　*For as long as I have breath, Lord,*
　　*I'll live my life for you,*
　　*And as long as I have strength, Lord,*
　　*I'll dance to worship you.*
　　(*Repeat chorus*)

2 My heart's so full of joy
　I cannot keep still,
　I'll dance upon the fresh green fields
　I'll jump the highest hill
　For you are my Creator,
　My Redeemer and my friend,
　You keep me by your love and grace,
　I'll praise you again and again.
　　*Chorus* (*twice*)

M. SMITH (b. 1948)

FAITHFUL VIGIL     6 5 6 5        David Wilson (b. 1940)

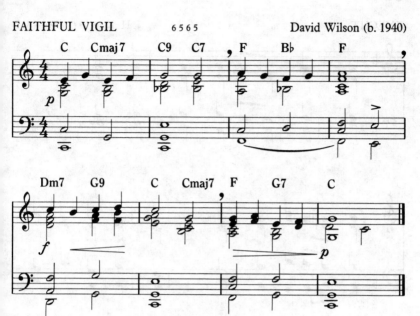

*From Luke 2:29—32 ('Nunc Dimittis')*

1 Faithful vigil ended,
  Watching, waiting cease;
  Master, grant thy servant
  His discharge in peace.

2 All thy Spirit promised,
  All the Father willed,
  Now these eyes behold it
  Perfectly fulfilled.

3 This thy great deliverence
  Sets thy people free;
  Christ their light uplifted
  All the nations see.

4 Christ, thy people's glory!
  Watching, doubting cease;
  Grant to us thy servants
  Our discharge in peace.

TIMOTHY DUDLEY-SMITH (b. 1926)

*See also No. 137, 'I lift my eyes'*

**88**

KNECHT     76. 76     J. H. Knecht (1752—1817)

1 Let us for ever praise him
  who heard us when we cried
  O come and praise our Saviour
  it was for us he died.

# PEACE

2 He found us when we sought him
   he gave our souls release
   he bore away our sorrows
   he is his people's peace.

3 Upon the cross in torment
   he set his people free
   from fear and condemnation
   for all eternity.

4 He knows the secret sadness
   which seems too great to bear
   the doubts and the resentments
   which we are loath to share.

5 He died that we might lose them
   it was his gift of love;
   O praise our dear Redeemer
   all other names above!

6 O praise him for his goodness!
   He understands our need;
   he is the Lord who made us;
   his peace is peace indeed.

DAVID PORTER (b. 1945)

# THE CHRISTIAN LIFE

# 89

ALL SCRIPTURES · Irregular

Michael Baughen (b. 1930)
arr. *W. Wooldridge*

## THE BIBLE

1 All Scriptures are given by the breath of God,
Are inspired of God,
Are the Word of the Lord;
All Scriptures are given by the breath of God,
And glorify his Name!

They can make you wise to a saving faith
In Jesus Christ the Lord;
They can make the man of God complete,
And are meant to be his sword!

2 So study to show yourself approved to God,
Fit to use his Word,
Fit to speak in his Name;
So study to show yourself approved to God,
A workman not ashamed.

They'll reprove, correct, and a training in
All righteous living afford;
They will yield up all that we need to know
Of the teaching of the Lord!

3 All Scriptures are given by the breath of God,
Are inspired of God,
Are the Word of the Lord;
All Scriptures are given by the breath of God,
And glorify his Name!

MICHAEL BAUGHEN (b. 1930)

# 90

YE BANKS AND BRAES  L.M.  Scottish Melody
arr. by Anthony Leach (b. 1947)

# THE BIBLE

1 May words of truth inform our minds
   That we may understand your will,
   And see, with open eyes, how best
   Your purposes we may fulfil.

2 May words of righteousness make plain
   How much our lives are spoiled by sin.
   Grant open ears that we may learn
   The way to conquer sin within.

3 May words of comfort, love and peace
   Dispel anxiety and care.
   Within open heart, filled from above,
   May loving deeds replace despair.

4 May words of life, from Christ our Lord,
   Give us each day a worthy aim.
   With ready hands, grant we may work
   With zeal to glorify his name.

PETER TONGEMAN (b. 1929)

**91**

WORDS     Irregular        Judy Mackenzie and David Cooke
*arr. Angela Reith*

## THE BIBLE

1 The world you made is full of words,
They pound our ears and eyes,
Hate words and great words,
And words of truth and lies,
Words that speak deceitfully,
And are not what they seem,
words that spell reality,
And words that sell a dream.
Help me to know what is true, Lord,
Help me to know what is true.

2 Your Word, O God, is sharper than
The sharpest two-edged sword,
It's law and fire and light, and points
To Christ the living Word.
Amid chaotic Babel sounds
Your Word alone can give
Me truth on which to stake my life
And show me how to live.
Help me to live by your Word, Lord,
Help me to live by your Word.

3 Your living Word already was
Before the world began.
The Word of life, the Word of light —
That Word became a man.
With healing hands and caring words
He spoke of liberty,
But very soon they captured him
And nailed him to a tree.
Praise him! He rose on the third day!
Praise him! He rose from the dead!

4 We sing you words of praise, Lord,
And yet our fervent song —
If this is where our worship ends —
Is like a noisy gong.
Unless we act upon your words
And love and care as well,
Our praise is empty, hollow, like
The clanging of a bell.
Help me to praise with my life, Lord,
Help me to live like you.

MICHAEL HEWS (b. 1925)

**92**

FIRST TUNE

FINEST GOLD          8 6 8 6 8 8 6          Ian Humphris (b. 1927)

# THE BIBLE

*All pairs of quavers are slurred in this item.*

# THE CHRISTIAN LIFE

## SECOND TUNE

**92**

HONEYCOMB     8 6 8 6 8 8 6     David Austin (b. 1932)

1 More precious than the finest gold
   The Bible is to me,
   And sweeter than the honeycomb
   Its promises can be.
   It is the sword within my hand,
   The map to show what God has planned,
   The lamp by which I see.

2 Compared with it no other book
   In all the world I find
   Has wisdom, goodness, power and love
   So wonderfully combined.
   It nerves the feeble will to fight
   And brings the truths of God to light
   In conscience, heart and mind.

3 O may this book increasingly
   Be precious in my sight —
   Its truth by day my counsellor,
   My comforter by night.
   Make it the ground on which I stand,
   And every promise and command
   The source of pure delight.

JOHN EDDISON (b. 1916)

*If the tune 'Finest Gold' is used the last line of each verse should be repeated.*

EPIPHANY HYMN  11.10.11.10.  Joseph Thrupp (1827–1867)

## THE BIBLE

1 Powerful in making us wise to salvation,
   witness to faith in Christ Jesus the Word;
   breathed out to men by the life-giving Father —
   these are the Scriptures, and thus speaks the Lord.

2 Tool for employment and compass for travel,
   map in the desert and lamp in the dark,
   teaching, rebuking, correcting, and training —
   these are the Scriptures, and this is their work.

3 Prophecy, history, and song, and commandment,
   Gospel and letter and dream from on high;
   written by men borne along by the Spirit —
   these are the Scriptures; on them we rely.

4 Gift for God's servants to fit them completely,
   fully equipping to walk in his ways;
   guide to good work and effective believing —
   these are the Scriptures; for these we give praise!

CHRISTOPHER IDLE (b. 1938)

**94**

OUR FATHER    8 5 8 5

Traditional Melody
*arr. by Robin Sheldon (b. 1932)*

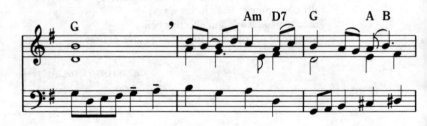

# PRAYER

## The Lord's Prayer

1 Our Father, who art in heaven,
   Hallowéd be thy name,
   Thy kingdom come, thy will be done,
   Hallowéd be thy name.

2 On earth as it is in heaven,
   Hallowéd be thy name,
   Give us this day our daily bread,
   Hallowéd be thy name.

3 Forgive us all our trespasses,
   Hallowéd be thy name,
   As we forgive those who trespass against us.
   Hallowéd by thy name.

4 And lead us not into temptation,
   Hallowéd be thy name,
   But deliver us from evil
   Hallowéd be thy name.

5 For thine is the kingdom, the power and the glory,
   Hallowéd be thy name,
   For ever and ever, for ever, Amen.
   Hallowéd be thy name.

Note—Owing to irregularities in the metre of verses 3, 4 & 5 the above lines require special attention. It is suggested that a choir or solo voice could sing the first three lines in these verses with the congregation joining in for the 4th.

**95**

FIRST TUNE

BAYSWATER    C.M.    Anthony Leach (b. 1947)

SECOND TUNE

WALDEN    C.M.    James E. Jones (1866—1939)

## PRAYER

1  This morning as I wait on thee
   Wilt thou reveal, dear Lord,
   Some message which thou hast for me
   Within thy holy word.

2  Then draw me closer still to thee
   In humble, earnest prayer,
   That those with whom I meet may see
   I've been with Jesus here.

3  So may I live this unknown day
   Beside thee from the start;
   Thy presence with me all the way,
   Thy word within my heart.

JOHN EDDISON (b. 1916)

WOLVERCOTE 7 6 7 6 D W. H. Ferguson (1874—1950)

*PRAYER*

1 Light of the minds that know him,
   May Christ be light to mine!
   My sun is risen splendour,
   My light of truth divine;
   My guide in doubt and darkness,
   My true and living way,
   My clear light ever shining,
   My dawn of heaven's day.

2 Life of the souls that love him,
   May Christ be ours indeed!
   The living bread from heaven
   On whom our spirits feed;
   Who died for love of sinners
   To bear our guilty load,
   And make of life's brief journey
   A new Emmaus road.

3 Strength of the wills that serve him,
   May Christ be strength to me,
   Who stilled the storm and tempest,
   Who calmed the tossing sea;
   His Spirit's power to move me,
   His will to master mine,
   His cross to carry daily
   And conquer in his sign.

4 May it be ours to know him
   That we may truly love,
   And loving, fully serve him
   As serve the saints above;
   Till in that home of glory
   With fadeless splendour bright,
   We serve in perfect freedom
   Our Strength, our Life, our Light.

TIMOTHY DUDLEY-SMITH (b. 1926)

**97**

SLANE 10.11.11.12.

Irish Traditional Melody
*harm. by Erik Routley (b. 1917)*

# PRAYER

1 Lord of all hopefulness, Lord of all joy,
  Whose trust, ever child-like, no cares could destroy,
  Be there at our wakening, and give us, we pray,
  Your bliss in our hearts, Lord, at the break of the day.

2 Lord of all eagerness, Lord of all faith,
  Whose strong hands were skilled at the plane and the lathe,
  Be there at our labours, and give us, we pray,
  Your strength in ʌur hearts, Lord, at the noon of the day.

3 Lord of all kindliness, Lord of all grace,
  Your hands swift to welcome, your arms to embrace,
  Be there at our homing, and give us, we pray,
  Your love in our hearts, Lord, at the eve of the day.

4 Lord of all gentleness, Lord of all calm,
  Whose voice is contentment, whose presence is balm,
  Be there at our sleeping, and give us, we pray,
  Your peace in our hearts, Lord, at the end of the day.

JAN STRUTHERS (1901-1953)

**98**

PENLAN      7 6 7 6 D          David Jenkins (1849—1915)

1 We seek, dear Lord, your presence,
   In Jesus' precious name,
   Our needs to lay before you,
   Your promises to claim.
   Take from us all distractions,
   Our wandering thoughts remove,
   That we in faith and meekness
   Your love and power may prove.

2 First, to ourselves as sinners,
   Your cleansing Lord impart,
   Remove the secret shadows
   Of sin from every heart.
   Then for ourselves as servants
   Your fullness Lord, we seek,
   Your grace to heal the broken,
   Your power to fill the meek.

3 Then lead us out, dear Master
   In interceding prayer,
   For those who do not know you,
   For those who do not care.
   In Satan's power and bondage,
   Asleep in sin they lie,
   Oh show them your salvation
   In answer to our cry.

4 With humble expectation
   We wait upon you now,
   In fuller, richer measure
   Your saving power to know;
   Then send us out, Lord Jesus,
   To labour on for you,
   Content to see your glory
   In hearts and lives made new.

JOHN EDDISON (b. 1916)

# 99

MOZART · 888888

Adapted from 'The Magic Flute'
W. A. Mozart (1756–91)

1 O Lamb of God whose perfect love,
In face of hate and human wrong,
Has found a way to meet my need
By patient suffering—silence strong!
I cannot pass your outstretched arms
To face a fate forlorn and long.

2 Your mercy pleads for my response,
Your grace abounding claims my soul,
Your seamless robe of righteousness
Can cover me and make me whole;
How can I try in naked shame
To brave the fight with sin's control?

3 I have no right to claim your aid,
Nor can I plead what I have done;
In your pure presence nothing hides
My secret sins, O searching Sun;
Yet you have overcome my sin
By victory already won!

4 Your death for sin has cancelled all
The shame and guilt you saw in me,
Your risen life of joy and peace
Is mine by glorious guarantee.
Your Spirit's seal I welcome now
And yield to love so glad and free.

RON PAVEY (b. 1913)

*See also No. 63 'Fire of God'.*

# 100

CHURCH TRIUMPHANT      L.M.      James W. Elliot (1833—1915)

1 When to our world the Saviour came
   The sick and helpless heard his Name,
   And in their weakness longed to see
   The healing Christ of Galilee.

2 That good physician! Night and day
   The people thronged about his way;
   And wonder ran from soul to soul —
   'The touch of Christ has made us whole.'

3 His praises then were heard and sung
   By opened ears and loosened tongue,
   While lightened eyes could see and know
   The healing Christ of long ago.

4 Of long ago — yet living still,
   Who died for us on Calvary's hill;
   Who triumphed over cross and grave,
   His healing hands stretched forth to save.

5 Those wounded hands are still the same,
   And all who serve that saving Name
   May share today in Jesus' plan—
   The healing Christ of everyman.

6 Then grant us, Lord, in this our day,
   To hear the prayers the helpless pray;
   Give to us hearts their pain to share,
   Make of us hands to tend and care.

7 Make us your hands! For Christ to live,
   In prayer and service, swift to give;
   Till all the world rejoice to find
   The healing Christ of all mankind.

TIMOTHY DUDLEY-SMITH (b. 1926)

*Written originally for the Centenary in 1978 of the
Medical Missionary Association*

**101**

GONFALON ROYAL     L.M.     Percy Buck (1871—1947)

1 Almighty Father, great must be
  Your power from all eternity;
  How great your love in Christ made known
  To those by suffering weighed down.

2 Christ healed the sick, the deaf, the blind,
   Brought reason to the splintered mind.
   He gave the peace of heaven to men
   And set them on their feet again.

3 Yet may these things for us be so,
   With Galilee those years ago?
   Is life and all its fullness still
   For us the heavenly Father's will?

4 Indeed! the Christ who wrought such things
   Is Lord of Lords and King of Kings:
   Today as yesterday the same
   To those who gather in his name.

5 Through laying on of hands and prayer
   The sick may in Christ's wholeness share,
   And others, nursed to health again,
   Renew their strength and lose their pain.

6 Almighty Father, let us see
   In Christ man has the victory!
   Help us to find, in life and death,
   Your everlasting arms beneath.

DAVID MOWBRAY (b. 1938)

**102**

WESTMINSTER        C.M.        James Turle (1802—1882)

1 He lives in us, the Christ of God,
  his Spirit joins with ours;
  he brings to us the Father's grace
  and powers beyond our powers.

2 And if enticing sin grows strong,
 when human nature fails,
 God's Spirit in our inner self
 fights with us, and prevails.

3 Our pangs of guilt and fears of death
 are Satan's strategems:
 by Jesus Christ who died for us
 God pardons; who condemns?

4 And when we cannot feel our faith
 nor bring ourselves to pray,
 the Spirit pleads with God for us
 in words we could not say.

5 God gave his Son to save us all —
 no other love like this! —
 then shall he ever turn away
 from those he marks as his?

6 And God has raised him from the grave,
 in this we stand assured;
 so none can tear us from his love
 in Jesus Christ our Lord.

MICHAEL PERRY (b. 1942)

**103**

ALBERTA      10.4 10.4 10.10.      William H. Harris (1883—1973)

*Original key Db

1 I do not ask for life the whole way through
  An easy road;
  Nor would I wish to seek O Lord from you
  A lighter load.
  Not for a smoother path, a fairer way,
  But for a greater strength, dear Lord, I pray.

2 I know that you did choose the hardest way
  Without regret;
  So teach me not to shrink from blood and tears,
  From toil and sweat.
  Nor would I ask for more than one reward —
  The knowledge that I do your will, O Lord.

3 I do not know what mountains must be scaled,
  What rivers crossed;
  I only look for strength to follow you
  What e'er the cost.
  I do not ask to see what you have planned,
  It is enough that you should take my hand.

4 The fight may well be stern and long, and yet,
  I must not fail;
  But I am weak, and in your strength alone
  Can I prevail.
  Yet in my weakness still your laws stand true
  That perfect strength is theirs who trust in you.

JOHN EDDISON (b. 1916)

*See also Nos. 128, 139*

**104**

GROWING     6 6 6 6         Robin Sheldon (b. 1932)

1 Now let us learn of Christ:
  He speaks, and we shall find
  He lightens our dark mind,
  So let us learn of Christ.

2 Now let us love in Christ
  As he has first loved us;
  As he endured the cross
  So let us love in Christ.

3 Now let us grow in Christ
  And look to things above
  And speak with truth and love,
  So let us grow in Christ.

4 Now let us stand in Christ
  In every trial we meet,
  In all his strength complete
  So let us stand in Christ.

CHRISTOPHER IDLE (b. 1938)

# 105

BEATITUDES

William Llewellyn (b. 1925)

NOTE: *Each bar whether $\frac{2}{4}$ or $\frac{3}{4}$ is to have the same duration.*

*f* Organ introduction

*f* ANTIPHON *(sung by all)*

Show us your ways, — O Lord, teach us your paths. ____

S *(Solo, or a few voices)*     A *(All, or full choir)*

1 *Blest are the poor__ in spi - rit;*     for theirs is the

# THE CHRISTIAN LIFE

king-dom of heav'n. 2 *Blest are they that mourn;*

for they shall be com - for - ted. 3 *Blest are the*

meek; for they shall in - he - rit the earth.

## GROWTH IN CHRIST

**ANTIPHON** *(sung by all)*

Show us your ways, __ O Lord, teach us your paths. __

**S** *(Solo)*

__ **4** *Blest are they that hun–ger and thirst af–ter*

**A** *(All or Choir)*

*right–eous–ness;* for they shall __ be filled.

# THE CHRISTIAN LIFE

5 Blest are the merciful; for they shall obtain mercy.

ANTIPHON *(sung by all)*

Show us your ways, O Lord, teach us your paths.

6 Blest are the pure in

# GROWTH IN CHRIST

A *(All or Choir)*

heart;     for they shall see God.

S *(Solo)*               A *(All or Choir)*

7 Blest are —— the peace - ma – kers;    for they shall be

S *(Solo)*

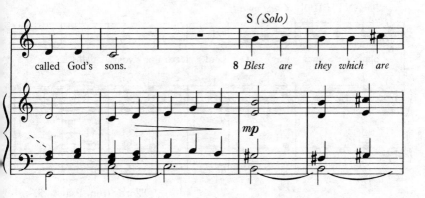

called God's sons.      8 Blest are they which are

# THE CHRISTIAN LIFE

*per - se - cu - ted      for      right - eous - ness'      sake;*

A *(All or Choir)*

*the      king - dom      of      heav'n      is      theirs.*

ANTIPHON *(sung by all)*

Show us your ways, — O Lord, teach us your paths. ——

Words from Psalm 25, v. 4
and Matthew 5, vv. 3—10

# GROWTH IN CHRIST

## THE BEATITUDES

ANTIPHON (sung by all)

**Show us your ways, O Lord, teach us your paths.**

S    *( Solo, or a few voices)*
   1  *Blest are the poor in spirit;*
A    (All, or full choir)
      for theirs is the kingdom of heaven.

S  2  *Blest are they that mourn;*
A    for they shall be comforted.

S  3  *Blest are the meek;*
A    for they shall inherit the earth.

ANTIPHON

S  4  *Blest are they that hunger and thirst after*
       *righteousness;*
A    for they shall be filled.

S  5  *Blest are the merciful;*
A    for they shall obtain mercy.

ANTIPHON

S  6  *Blest are the pure in heart;*
A    for they shall see God.

S  7  *Blest are the peacemakers;*
A    for they shall be called God's sons.

S  8  *Blest are they which are persecuted*
      *for righteousness' sake;*
A    the kingdom of heaven is theirs.

ANTIPHON

*The Beatitudes may of course be sung through without the above
suggestions for variety in vocal groups.*

*'Antiphon' is an ancient term referring to a congregational
refrain interpolated between verses of a psalm which were sung
in time by different sections of the choir; hence the more well
known word 'antiphon'.*

# 106

I WANT TO WALK          10.7 10.8 and refrain          Kathleen Thomerson
(b. 1934)

1  I want to walk as a child of the light.
   I want to follow Jesus.
   God set the stars to give light to the world.
   The star of my life is Jesus.
   *In him there is no darkness at all,*
   *The night and the day are both alike.*
   *The Lamb is the light of the city of God.*
   *Shine in my heart, Lord Jesus.*

2  I want to see the brightness of God.
   I want to look at Jesus.
   Clear sun of righteousness, shine on my path,
   And show me the way to the Father.
   *Refrain*

3  I'm looking for the coming of Christ.
   I want to be with Jesus.
   When we have run with patience the race,
   We shall know the joy of Jesus.
   *Refrain*

KATHLEEN THOMERSON (b. 1934)

*See also No. 119*

**107**

BLEST ARE THE POOR        6 6 8 6 D        Fr. Gerard Beaumont, C.R.
(1903—1970)

**Light and bouncy**

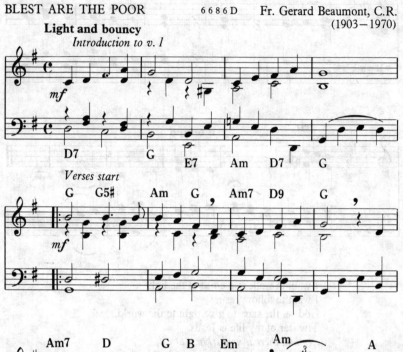

## GROWTH IN CHRIST

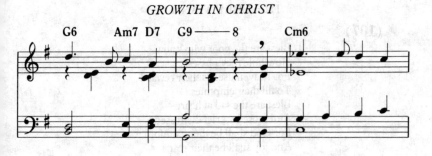

**(107)**

1 Blest are the poor who know
How little they possess,
For heaven itself is their reward
To fill their emptiness.
Blest are the sad at heart—
And those by grief distressed,
For God shall be their comforter,
And joy shall be their rest.

2 Blest are the gentle souls,
Unvexed by worldly cares,
Who walk in ways of lowliness,
For all the earth is theirs.
Blest are all they who thirst
And hunger for the right;
They shall be satisfied with good
Who in the truth delight.

3 Blest are the merciful,
Compassionate, and kind,
For in the mercy that they show
They too shall mercy find.
Blest are the pure in heart
Who guilelessly have trod
In innocence the path of life,
For they shall see their God.

4 Blest are those making peace,
Who curb the lust of wars;
They shall be called the Sons of God
And heaven's inheritors.
And blest are they whom hate
And persecution's sword
Strikes as they battle for the truth,
For heaven is their reward.

5 Blest are you when reviled,
And blest when men shall make
False accusations, blaming you
With evil for my sake.
Rejoice exceedingly,
For great is your reward;
Of old they persecuted thus
The Prophets of the Lord.

GERARD BEAUMONT (d. 1970)

**108**

TELL OUT MY SOUL      10.10.10.10.      Michael Baughen

Hymn — *Tell out, my soul, the greatness of the Lord!* and second tune
'*Woodlands*' is set overleaf

# 108

WOODLANDS      10.10.10.10.      Walter Greatorex (1877–1949)

1 Tell out, my soul, the greatness of the Lord!
 Unnumbered blessings, give my spirit voice;
 Tender to me the promise of his word;
 In God my Saviour shall my heart rejoice.

2 Tell out, my soul, the greatness of his Name!
 Make known his might, the deeds his arm
 has done;
 His mercy sure, from age to age the same;
 His Holy Name — the Lord, the Mighty One.

3 Tell out, my soul, the greatness of his might!
 Powers and dominions lay their glory by.
 Proud hearts and stubborn wills are put to flight,
 The hungry fed, the humble lifted high.

4 Tell out, my soul, the glories of his word!
 Firm is his promise, and his mercy sure.
 Tell out, my soul, the greatness of the Lord
 To children's children and for evermore!

TIMOTHY DUDLEY-SMITH (b. 1926)

GO, TELL          Irregular                    *arr. by P. C. Butler*

*Go tell it on the mountain,*
*Over the hills and ev'rywhere.*
*Go tell it on the mountain,*
*That Jesus Christ is Lord.*

1 Oh when I was a seeker,
  I sought both night and day.
  I asked the Lord to help me,
  And he showed me the way.
    *Chorus*

2 He made me a watchman,
  Upon the city wall;
  To tell of his salvation,
  For Jesus died for all.
    *Chorus*

3 Go tell it to your neighbour,
  In darkness here below;
  Go with the words of Jesus,
  That all the world may know.
    *Chorus*

P. C. BUTLER

GOD'S SPIRIT    Irregular    Hubert Richards

## SERVICE—WITNESS

# THE CHRISTIAN LIFE

1 God's spirit is in my heart,
   He has called me and set me apart,
   This is what I have to do,
   What I have to do.
   *He sent me to give the good news to the poor,*
   *Tell prisoners that they are prisoners no more,*
   *Tell blind people that they can see,*
   *And set the downtrodden free.*
   *And go tell everyone the news,*
   *That the Kingdom of God has come!*
   *And go tell everyone the news,*
   *That God's Kingdom has come.*

2 Just as the Father sent me
   So I'm sending you out to be
   My witness throughout the world
   The whole of the world.
   *Chorus*

3 Don't carry a load in your pack
   You don't need two shirts to your back.
   A workman can earn his own keep,
   Can earn his own keep.
   *Chorus*

4 Don't worry what you have to say
   Don't worry because on that day
   God's spirit will speak in your heart
   Will speak in your heart.
   *Chorus*

ALAN DALE

# 111

ST. FRANCIS  Irregular

Sebastian Temple
*arr. by Betty Pulkingham* (b.1925)

**Flowing**

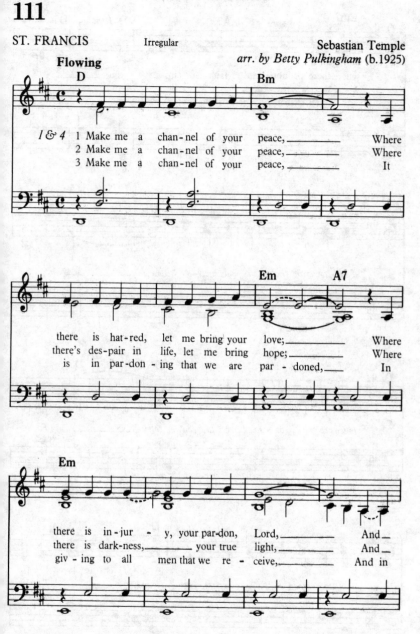

1 & 4  1 Make me a chan-nel of your peace,_____ Where
2 Make me a chan-nel of your peace,_____ Where
3 Make me a chan-nel of your peace,_____ It

there is hat-red, let me bring your love;_____ Where
there's des-pair in life, let me bring hope;_____ Where
is in par-don-ing that we are par-doned,_____ In

there is in-jur-y, your par-don, Lord,_____ And_
there is dark-ness,_____ your true light,_____ And_
giv-ing to all men that we re-ceive,_____ And in

Reprinted by permission of the Franciscan Communications Center, Los Angeles, Calif. 1975.

# THE CHRISTIAN LIFE

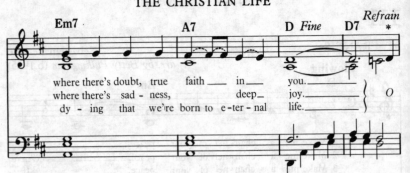

where there's doubt, true faith ___ in ___ you. ___
where there's sad - ness, deep _ joy. ___
dy - ing that we're born to e - ter - nal life. ___  O

Mas - ter, grant that I may nev - er seek, ___ So

much to be con - soled as to con - sole; ___ To be

un - der - stood as to un - der - stand; ___ To be

*Voices may sing in two-part harmony.*

## SERVICE—WITNESS

*loved    as    to    love with all    my    soul.*

1  Make me a channel of your peace,
    Where there is hatred, let me bring your love,
    Where there is injury, your pardon, Lord,
    And where there's doubt, true faith in you.
      *O Master, grant that I may never seek,*
      *So much to be consoled as to console,*
      *To be understood as to understand,*
      *To be loved as to love with all my soul.*

2  Make me a channel of your peace,
    Where there's despair in life, let me bring hope,
    Where there is darkness, your true light,
    And where there's sadness, your deep joy.
      *Refrain*

3  Make me a channel of your peace,
    It is in pardoning that we are pardoned,
    In giving to all men that we receive,
    And in dying that we are born to eternal life.
      *Refrain*

4  Make me a channel of your peace,
    Where there is hatred, let me bring your love,
    Where there is injury, your pardon, Lord,
    And where there's doubt, true faith in you.

*Based on a prayer of*
**ST. FRANCIS OF ASSISI**

**112**

BALMORAL  8 7 8 7  William Davies (b. 1921

## SERVICE—WITNESS

1 Jesus, Man who lived for others,
  Formed a servant at your birth,
  Help us now to serve by being
  Neighbour to each man on earth.

2 As the good man of Samaria
  Helped the victim by the way,
  Gave his beast and coins and kindness,
  May we recognise today

3 Neighbours in the lonely exiles
  Driven from their homes and land,
  Victims of a world in turmoil,
  Reaching for our caring hand;

4 Neighbours in the men whose hunger
  Makes of life a struggle grim,
  Needy in a world of plenty,
  Brothers we can serve for him;

5 So may we by gifts and caring
  Serve a world that, growing small,
  Fashions every man a neighbour
  Making brothers of us all.

6 Jesus, Man who lived for others,
  Formed a servant at your birth,
  Help us now to serve by being
  Neighbour to each man on earth.

KENNETH SLACK (b. 1917)

**113**

STRENGTH AND STAY  11.10.11.10.  J. B. Dykes (1823–1876)
*Re-harmonized by Robin Sheldon (b. 1932)*

1 O loving Lord, who art for ever seeking
  Men of thy mind, intent to do thy will,
  Strong in thy strength, thy power and grace bespeaking,
  Faithful to thee through good report and ill.

2 To thee we come, and humbly make confession,
  Faithless so oft, in thought and word and deed,
  Asking that we may have, in true possession,
  Thy free forgiveness in the hour of need.

3 In duties small, be thou our inspiration,
  In large affairs endue us with thy might;
  Through faithful service cometh full salvation,
  So may we serve, thy will our chief delight.

4 Not disobedient to the heavenly vision,
  Faithful in all things, seeking not reward,
  Then, following thee, may we fulfil our mission,
  True to ourselves, our brethren, and our Lord.

WILLIAM VAUGHAN JENKINS (d. 1920)

**114**

ABRIDGE     C.M.     Isaac Smith (1734—1805)

## GUIDANCE AND STRENGTH

1 Give me, dear Lord, the power I need
  To live this day aright;
  May every thought and word and deed
  Be pleasing in your sight.

2 Give me your sympathy today
  For those whom I shall meet,
  Who walk a hard and lonely way
  With sad and weary feet.

3 Give me your wisdom too for those
  With charm and humour too,
  And yet whose every action shows
  They have no place for you.

4 Your patience too for those, I plead,
  Who can't believe it's true
  That all their great exceeding need
  Can still be met by you.

6 But richer than your gifts in this:—
  The fact of who you are;
  Compared with them your presence is
  More wonderful by far.

JOHN EDDISON (b. 1916)

**115**

DOWNLAND     8 6 8 6 8 6     Robin Sheldon (b. 1932)

*From Rom. 8:28*

1 Father, although I cannot see
   The future you have planned,
   And though the path is sometimes dark
   And hard to understand;
   Yet give me faith, through joy and pain
   To trace your loving hand.

2 When I recall that in the past
   Your promises have stood
   Through each perplexing circumstance
   And every changing mood,
   I rest content that all things work
   Together for my good.

3 And so, whate'er the future brings
   Of good or seeming ill,
   I ask for strength to follow you
   And grace to trust you still;
   And I would look for no reward,
   Except to do your will.

JOHN EDDISON (b. 1916)

GOODWIN—HUDSON      C.M.      Anthony Leach (b. 1947)

1 Show me your measured plan, O Lord,
  Make clear your way to me
  That, seeing what is good, I may
  Pursue it constantly.

2 Teach me to build my life, O Lord,
  Secure upon your Word
  That, founded deep, it may withstand
  All evil undeterred.

3 Build strong an inner framework, Lord,
  Well shaped by your demands
  That every corner of my life
  May yield to your commands.

4 Let doors of entrance, Lord, be given
  To truth that you impart.
  Let love of all things pure and good
  Dwell in my mind and heart.

5 Let windows open, Lord, to light
  That shines warm from above
  Illuminating every task
  With holy, Christ-like love.

6 Build lastingly as to the Word
  Of truth I daily look,
  And furnish me with everything
  As in your holy Book.

PETER TONGEMAN (b. 1929)

**117**

ST. LEONARD      8 7 8 7 7 7      Melody by J. C. Bach (1642—1703)

1  Men of God whose faith abounded
   Have their victories told aloud;
   By such witnesses surrounded,
   Christ's unseen, uncounted crowd,
   We take up th' unfinished race
   Chosen, trained, inspired by grace.

2  Confident and persevering,
   Firmly let us run to win,
   Stripped of all the interfering
   Rags and shreds of stubborn sin;
   Still on Jesus fix our eyes,
   Faith's foundation and its prize.

3  Jesus, for the joy before him
   Made a crown of thorns his own,
   Seated now where we adore him
   High upon his Father's throne;
   See the shame which he endured,
   Share the triumph he secured.

CHRISTOPHER IDLE (b. 1938)

# 118

YOUR LOVE 884 D Helen Wickham (b. 1949)

*This tune is more suitable for use with guitar accompaniment than with the organ.*

# DEDICATION

1 Your love, O Christ, is near to me,
Your presence now is dear to me,
You are my king.
The world for you was unprepared,
A cattle shed was all they cared,
How poor my part.

2 So, Lord, I'll keep a room for you,
I'll sweep it with my broom for you:
It is my heart.
You found it full of dirt and sin,
I failed to keep it pure within,
I gave my best.

3 So now I bring this heart to you,
With tears of faith I shed for you,
For peace and rest.
Your love like sun shall brightly shine
When you live in this heart of mine.
Be now my guest.

CHRISTOPHER PORTEOUS (b. 1935)

*See also No. 97*

# 119

WALKING      Irregular

Swiss Folk Tune
*arr. Betty Pulkingham (b. 1928)*

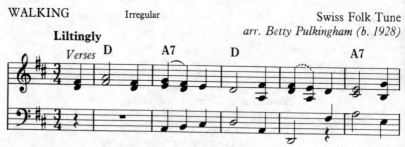

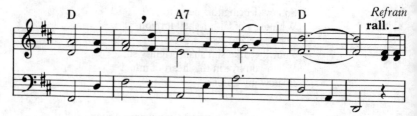

## DEDICATION

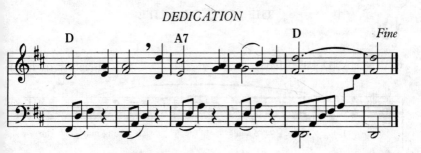

1 I want to walk with Jesus Christ,
   All the days I live of this life on earth,
   To give to him complete control
   Of body and of soul.

   *Follow him, follow him, yield your life to him,*
   *He has conquered death, he is King of Kings,*
   *Accept the joy which he gives to those*
   *Who yield their lives to him.*

2 I want to learn to speak to him,
   To pray to him, confess my sin,
   To open my life and let him in,
   For joy will then be mine.
       *Refrain*

3 I want to learn to speak to him,
   My life must show that he lives in me.
   My deeds, my thoughts, my words must speak
   All of his love for me.
       *Refrain*

4 I want to learn to read his word,
   For this is how I know the way
   To live my life as pleases him,
   In holiness and joy.
       *Refrain*

5 O Holy Spirit of the Lord,
   Enter now into this heart of mine,
   Take full control of my selfish will
   And make me wholly thine.
       *Refrain*

ST. PAUL'S (ERITH) 1964
Swiss Houseparty

**120**

GIVING AND KEEPING    Irregular    S. I. Houghton (b. 1902)

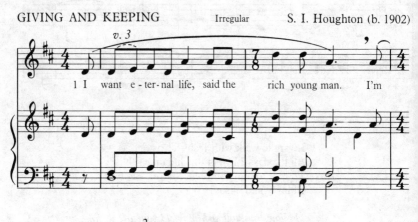

1 I want e-ter-nal life, said the rich young man. I'm

sure I've done the best____ that an-y-one can.

What must I do? said the rich young man.

# GIVING

I will give you life if you'll fol-low where I lead, But

first sell all you have and give to those in need,

*v. 2*

This Je-sus said to the rich young man.

# THE CHRISTIAN LIFE

And he turned a-way sad, ve-ry ve-ry sad, For he

wan-ted to keep all he had.

1 I want eternal life, said the rich young man.
I'm sure I've done the best that anyone can.
What must I do? said the rich young man.
I will give you life if you'll follow where I lead,
But first sell all you have and give to those in need,
This Jesus said to the rich young man.
And he turned away sad, very very sad,
For he wanted to keep all he had.

2 The people are in need, and they must be fed;
  Is anyone here who will give me bread?
  Here is my lunch, so the little boy said.
  Jesus thus was able to feed the multitude.
  For in his loving hands was good supply of food;
  More than enough, so everyone said.
  So the boy went home very, very glad,
  For to Jesus he gave all he had.

3 A poor little widow with heart full of love,
  Just longed to please her Father up above.
  What would she do to show her love?
  Hardly any money had she on which to live,
  But holding nothing back, most gladly she would give,
  In gratitude to the God above.
  It made Jesus feel glad, very, very glad,
  For her love made her give all she had.

4 How little did they know as he passed their way
  The joy that would be theirs on Resurrection Day,
  Their gifts of love he would soon repay.
  Had they heard him say, 'In heaven put your treasure;
  If your hearts are there, then your gifts you'll not measure.'
  Now after all they are glad, so glad,
  That they gave while on earth all that they had
  To Jesus who passed by their way.

S. I. HOUGHTON (b. 1902)

* *all syllables to be sung exactly against notes as written, even though accents seem unusual.*

# 121

LONG AND LONELY DAYS    Irregular    John Lockley
*arr. by Rob. Stoodley*

In the long and lone-ly days when it seems
That an - y - thing be - yond is just a fig - ment of my
dreams. And the on - ly hope I find Lies with - in my seeth-ing

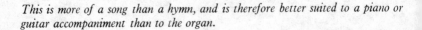

*This is more of a song than a hymn, and is therefore better suited to a piano or guitar accompaniment than to the organ.*

## SEARCHING FOR GOD

mind, He speaks to me of God.

2 When the 4 fol - low him, to fol - low

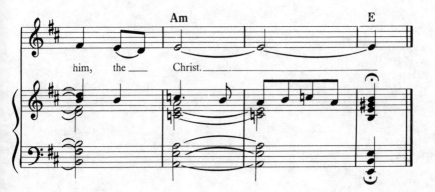

him, the ___ Christ. ___

# THE CHRISTIAN LIFE

1 In the long and lonely days when it seems
   That anything beyond is just a figment of my dreams.
   And the only hope I find
   Lies within my seething mind,
   He speaks to me of God.

2 When the hoardings scream their lies to the world,
   And penetrating fogs of dark uncertainty have swirled
   Round within my brain so long
   That what once seemed right is wrong,
   He speaks to me of truth.

3 When the sufferings of man fill my eyes,
   And all the sounds of earth contain no laughter, only cries,
   And it seems that fear and hate
   Are the rulers of our fate,
   He speaks to me of love.

4 He proclaims to us what we can still be
   By showing in himself a vision clear for all to see
   Of the way to live and die;
   And it seems that we must try
   To follow him, to follow him, the Christ.

PETER CASEY (b. 1948)

# 122

SEARCH FOR THE INFANT  Irregular  Paul Carter

Music and words: © 1972 by Hye-Fye Music Ltd.; from 'Carols for Children'

# THE CHRISTIAN LIFE

1, 2 & 3

1 & 3

*vvs. 1–3*  *Link between verses*

*v. 4*

Je - sus does reign.

*rall.*

## SEARCHING FOR GOD

1 Search for the infant born in a stable,
  Search where it's humble, search where it's poor.
  Man's search for God finds rest in a stable,
  There in the smell and warmth of the straw.
  See the infant, what a wonder!
  See the mother's tender care.
  Cow and ass stand close together,
  While their bodies warm the air.

2 Search for the man who travels the country,
  Feeding the hungry, healing the blind.
  Man's search for God finds rest in the needy,
  There with the outcasts of every kind.
  There the word of love is spoken,
  There the truth of God made clear,
  In the country, up on the hillside,
  People in thousands jostle to hear.

3 Search for the man who hangs on a gallows,
  Nailed there by hatred, nailed there by fear.
  Man's search for God finds rest at the gallows,
  There at the cross the answer is near.
  Hear the mocking, hear the scorning,
  See the blood and feel the pain.
  On the hilltop, nailed to the gallows,
  Love meets rejection, all seems in vain.

4 Search for the man who's risen for ever,
  Out on the highway, down by the shore.
  Man's search for God finds truth in his spirit,
  Still with the needy, still with the poor.
  Where there's hunger, where there's hatred,
  Where injustice, where there's pain,
  Out of the stable, out of the country,
  Down from the gallows, Jesus does reign.

ROY WARD

**123**

FREEDOM SONG     Irregular     Angela Reith (b. 1952)

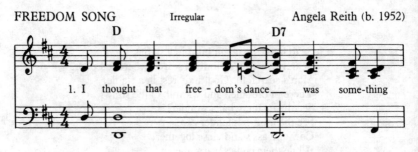

1. I thought that free-dom's dance___ was some-thing

I could or-gan-ize: That some-one else would

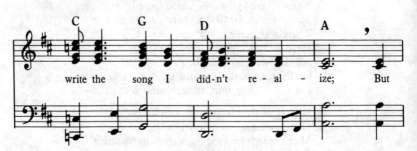

write the song I did-n't re-al-ize; But

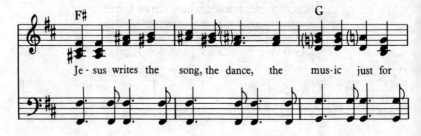

Je-sus writes the song, the dance, the mus-ic just for

# FREEDOM IN CHRIST

1 I thought that freedom's dance was something I could organise,
   That someone else would write the song I didn't realise,
   But Jesus writes the song, the dance, the music just for me,
   And in being slave to him discover that I'm free:
      *I'm in the dance with him,*
      *I'm in the dance with him,*
      *I'm in the dance and I'm free;*
      *Come on and dance with him,*
      *Come on and dance with him,*
      *Join in the dance and be free.*

2 The freedom song of Jesus isn't one you sing alone,
   But with the most astounding choir the world has ever known.
   All colours are our brothers, and there's hope of harmony,
   And bosses join with workers in the Jesus family.
      *Chorus*

3 The freedom song of Jesus is for sharing far and wide:
   The music of the way he lived, the song of why he died;
   The dance of resurrection joy that Jesus lives today;
   It's a rhapsody for sharing from Belfast to Bombay:
      *Chorus*

4 The freedom song of Jesus is a song of war and peace:
   To the lonely and the frightened it's the music of release,
   But in war against injustice it's the battle song to sing,
   The battle-song to march to in the name of Christ the King:
      *Chorus*

MICHAEL HEWS (b. 1925)
DAVID LEWIS
RIKKI SEFTON (b. 1959)

**124**

SOMERSET HILLS     L.M.     Lee Hastings Bristol, Jr. (b. 1923)

1 Lord of the home, thine only Son
  Received a mother's tender love;
  And from an earthly father won
  His vision of thy home above.

2 Help us, O Lord, our homes to make
  Thy Holy Spirit's dwelling place;
  Our hands and hearts devotion take
  To be the servant of thy grace.

3 Lord, may thy Spirit sanctify
  Each household duty we fulfil,
  May we our Master glorify
  In glad obedience to thy will.

ALBERT BAYLY (b. 1901)

**125**

HOLY FAITH          888888                    G. C. Martin (1844—1916)

*Continued*

# THE HOME

*Harmony*

1 Father on high to whom we pray
  And lift our thankful hearts above,
  For all your mercies day by day,
  For gifts of hearth and home and love —
  Protect them still beneath your care:
  Lord in your mercy, hear our prayer.

2 O Christ who came as man to earth
  And chose in Egypt's land to be
  A homeless child of alien birth,
  An exile and a refugee —
  For homeless people everywhere,
  Lord in your mercy, hear our prayer.

3 Spirit divine, whose work is done
  In souls renewed and lives restored,
  Strive in our hearts to make us one,
  One faith, one family, one Lord —
  Till at the last one home we share:
  Lord in your mercy, hear our prayer.

TIMOTHY DUDLEY-SMITH (b. 1926)

# 126

TRUMPET VOLUNTARY    6 9 6 8 and refrain    melody Jeremiah Clarke
*arr. by Robin Sheldon (b. 1932)*

*This can be played in G major when there is a predominance of lower voices, but
it has more thrust in A major.*

1  This earth belongs to God,
     The world, its wealth, and all its people:
     He formed the waters wide
     And fashioned every sea and shore.
       *Who may go up the hill of the Lord*
       *And stand in the place of holiness?*
       *Only the man whose heart is pure,*
       *Whose hands and lips are clean.*

2  Lift high your heads, you gates,
     Rise up, you everlasting doors, as
     Here now the King of glory
     Enters into full command.
       *Who is the King, this King of glory,*
       *Where is the throne he comes to claim?*
       *Christ is the King, the Lord of glory,*
       *Fresh from his victory.*

3  Lift high your heads, you gates,
     And fling wide open the ancient doors, for
     Here comes the King of glory
     Taking universal power.
       *Who is the King, this King of glory,*
       *What is the power by which he reigns?*
       *Christ is the King, his cross his glory,*
       *And by love he rules.*

4  All glory be to God
     The Father, Son, and Holy Spirit;
     From ages past it was,
     Is now, and evermore shall be.

CHRISTOPHER IDLE (b. 1938)

# 127

DAM BUSTERS MARCH 7 7 7 5 7 8 11.

Eric Coates
*arr. by Robin Sheldon (b. 1932)*

1 God is our strength and refuge,
Our present help in trouble;
And we therefore will not fear,
Though the earth should change!
Though mountains shake and tremble,
Though swirling waters are raging,
God the Lord of Hosts is with us evermore!

2 There is a flowing river,
Within God's holy city;
God is in the midst of her,
She shall not be moved!
God's help is swiftly given,
Thrones vanish at his presence;
God the Lord of Hosts is with us evermore!

3 Come, see the works of our Maker,
Learn of his deeds all powerful;
Wars will cease across the world
When he shatters the spear!
Be still and know your creator,
Uplift him in the nations;
God the Lord of Hosts is with us evermore!

RICHARD BEWES (b. 1934)

**128**

MERCIFUL AND GRACIOUS 777777 Norman Warren (b. 1934)

1  Merciful and gracious be,
   O Most High, remember me.
   When my enemies assail
   May your grace and power prevail.
   Keep me in the day of fear
   Firm in faith that God is near.

2  When they wait to do me wrong,
   Plan my hurt the whole day long,
   Twist my words and mark my way,
   Seek my life — O Lord, repay!
   Wither them beneath your frown;
   In displeasure cast them down.

3  Lord, you know my days and years,
   All my wanderings, all my tears;
   What though man would work me ill,
   God himself will keep me still
   In his light, through length of days,
   Firm to stand and strong to praise.

TIMOTHY DUDLEY-SMITH (b. 1926)

**129**

CASWALL       6 5 6 5       Friedrich Filitz (1804—1876)

1  Listen to my prayer, Lord,
   Hear my humble cry;
   When my heart is fainting,
   To your throne I fly.

2  In earth's farthest corner
   You will hear my voice;
   Set me on your rock, Lord,
   Then I shall rejoice.

3  You have been my shelter
   When the foe was near,
   As a tower of refuge
   Shielding me from fear.

4  I will rest for ever
   In your care and love,
   Guarded and protected
   As by wings above.

5  All that I have promised,
   Help me to fulfil;
   And in all who love You
   Work your perfect will.

6  May your truth and mercy
   Keep me all my days;
   Let my words and actions
   Be my songs of praise.

J. E. SEDDON (b. 1915)

# 130

# GOD IN THE PSALMS

HOW LOVELY     12.11.12.11.            David Wilson

Alternative tune: 'The Streets of Laredo' (Youth Praise II, No. 163)

1 How lovely, how lovely, the place of your dwelling
  O Lord God of heaven, the Lord of all life!
  My soul longs and faints just to live in your presence,
  My heart and my flesh sing for joy to the Lord.

2 The sparrow is welcome; the swallow is nesting;
  They both find a haven to nurture their young.
  For them and your people, O Lord King of heaven,
  Your altars give blessing, your presence gives praise.

3 The man truly happy is praising God always
  The man truly strong finds his strength in the Lord,
  And deep in his heart is the pathway to heaven
  He travels the desert and finds there a spring.

4 The strength of believers grows on without limit
  And God's work is seen in the lives of his saints.
  O Lord God of heaven, the shield of our fathers,
  Attend to our prayers and shine out in our hearts.

5 O God, how much better one day in your presence
  Than days by the thousand in earth's fairest place.
  Far better to linger in your temple's doorway
  Than live in a place in which evil holds sway.

6 The Lord is a sun and a shield to his people
  If we give obedient heed to his laws.
  The things worth possessing, he gladly will give us
  How blest is the man who will trust in the Lord.

JONATHAN BARNES

# 131

GOD IN THE PSALMS

INVITATION TO WORSHIP 11.10.11.10.

Michael Perry (b. 1942)
*arr. S. K. Coates*

*for easier guitar chords in G see melody edition.*

## BASED ON *PSALM 95 (VENITE)*

*after last verse only*

1 Come worship God who is worthy of honour,
  Enter his presence with thanks and a song;
  He is the Rock of his people's salvation,
  To whom our jubilant praises belong.

2 Ruled by his might are the heights of the
      mountains,
  Held in his hands are the depths of the earth,
  His is the sea, his the land; for he made them,
  King above all gods, who gave man his birth.

3 We are his people, the sheep of his pasture,
  He is our Maker and to him we pray,
  Gladly we kneel in obedience
      before him—
  Great is the God whom we worship this day!

4 Now let us listen, for God speaks among us,
  Open our hearts and receive what he says;
  Peace be to all who remember his goodness,
  Trust in his promises, walk in his ways.
  Come worship God who is worthy of honour!

MICHAEL PERRY (b. 1942)

# GOD IN THE PSALMS

**132**

SING HOSANNA       10.9 10.9 and chorus

*Traditional*
*arr. Norman Warren (b. 1934)*

Let us sing to the God of sal-va-tion,___ Let us sing to the Lord our

rock! Let us come to His house with thanksgiving___. Let us

*Chorus*

come be-fore the Lord and sing! *Praise* our Ma-ker, *Praise* our Sa-viour,

*Praise* the Lord our ev-er - last-ing King. *Ev* - *ry* throne must

## BASED ON PSALM 95 (VENITE)

*A simpler version of this tune (in E♭) can be found at No. 85*

1 Let us sing to the God of salvation,
  Let us sing to the Lord our rock!
  Let us come to his house with thanksgiving!
  Let us come before the Lord and sing!
    *Praise our Maker,*
    *Praise our Saviour,*
    *Praise the Lord our everlasting King.*
    *Every throne must bow before him,*
    *God is Lord of everything!*

2 In his hand are the earth's deep places
  And the strength of the hills is his!
  All the sea is the Lord's, for he made it,
  By his hands the dry land was formed.
    *Chorus*

3 Let us worship the Lord our Maker,
  Let us kneel to the Lord our God;
  For we all are the sheep of his pasture,
  He will guide us by his powerful hand.
    *Chorus*

4 Let today be the time when you hear him!
  May our hearts not be hard or cold,
  Lest we stray from the Lord in rebellion,
  As his people did in time of old.
    *Chorus*

RICHARD BEWES (b. 1934)

CHORAL SYMPHONY      8 7 8 7 D      Beethoven (1770−1827)
*arr. Robin Sheldon (b. 1932)*

*vvs. 1 & 2*

*A simpler version in F may be found in* Psalm Praise *No. 27*

1 Sing to God new songs of worship —
  All his deeds are marvellous;
  He has brought salvation to us
  With his hand and holy arm.
  He has shown to all the nations
  Righteousness and saving power;
  He recalled his truth and mercy
  To his people Israel.

2 Sing to God new songs of worship —
  Earth has seen his victory;
  Let the lands of Earth be joyful
  Praising him with thankfulness.
  Sound upon the harp his praises,
  Play to him with melody —
  Let the trumpets sound his triumph,
  Show your joy to God the King.

3 Sing to God new songs of worship —
  Let the sea now make a noise;
  All on earth and in the waters
  Sound your praises to the Lord.
  Let the hills be joyful together,
  Let the rivers clap their hands,
  For with righteousness and justice
  He will come to judge the Earth.

MICHAEL BAUGHEN (b. 1930)

# 134

JUBILATE EVERYBODY     8 6 8 6 7 8     Michael Perry (b. 1942)
*arr. S. C. Coates and Norman Warren (b. 1934)*

BASED ON *PSALM 100 (JUBILATE)*

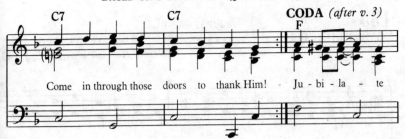

## JUBILATE—'O Be Joyful'

1 Jubilate everybody,
  Serve the Lord with gladness;
  O be joyful everybody
  Come before him singing.
  *Come into his church with praise*
  *Come in through those doors to thank him!*

2 Know that He, the God who made us,
  He it is who owns us;
  We, the people of his care,
  The sheep upon his hillside.
  *Come into his church with praise*
  *Come in through those doors to thank him!*

3 For the Lord our God is good —
  His love is everlasting;
  And his faithfulness endures
  To every generation.
  *Come into his church with praise*
  *Come in through those doors to thank him!*

  Jubilate everybody,
  Jubilate De-o!

MICHAEL PERRY (b. 1942)

# GOD IN THE PSALMS

**135**

COME REJOICE 1

FIRST TUNE

8 7 8 7

David G. Wilson (b. 1940)
*arr. Norman Warren (b. 1934)*

© D. G. Wilson

SECOND TUNE

COME REJOICE 2          8 7 8 7          Noel Tredinnick

1 Come, rejoice before your Maker
  All you peoples of the Earth;
  Serve the Lord your God with gladness,
  Come before him with a song!

2 Know for certain that Jehovah
  Is the true and only God;
  We are his, for he has made us —
  We are sheep within his fold.

3 Come with grateful hearts before him,
  Enter now his courts with praise;
  Show your thankfulness towards him,
  Give due honour to his Name.

4 For the Lord our God is gracious —
  Everlasting in his love,
  And to every generation
  His great faithfulness endures.

MICHAEL BAUGHEN (b. 1930)

Michael Baughen (b. 1930)
arr. *David G. Wilson (b. 1940)*

BLESS THE LORD     Irregular

**With strong rhythm but not too fast**

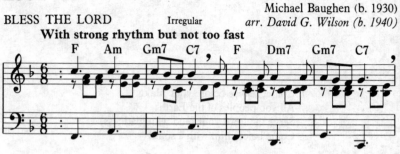

*last time to CODA* ⊕

⊕*CODA* **Slower**

1  Bless the Lord, O my soul,
   And all within me, honour his Name!
   Bless the Lord, O my soul,
   And never forget all his blessings.

     He forgives all your sin
     And he heals all your ills,
     He redeems your life from the pit,
     He shows mercy upon you
     And steadfast love,
     He renews your youth by good things.

2  Bless the Lord, O my soul,
   And all within me, honour his Name!
   Bless the Lord, O my soul,
   And never forget all his blessings.

     Justice for the oppressed
     With compassion and grace,
     Slow to anger, abounding in love —
     He is not always chiding
     But in his love
     He does not remember our sins.

3.  As the heavens are high
   To those who fear him, his love is great.
   As the East from the West
   So far he removes our sins from us.

     Days of man are like grass
     Or a flower of the field;
     As the wind passes over, it goes.
     But on those who obey him
     With steadfast love
     He bestows his love evermore.

4  Bless the Lord, King of All!
   All you his angels doing his word!
   Bless the Lord, all his hosts,
   And all of his works in creation.
   Bless the Lord, O my soul!

MICHAEL BAUGHEN (b. 1930)

**137**

LIFT MY EYES Irregular Michael Baughen (b. 1930)

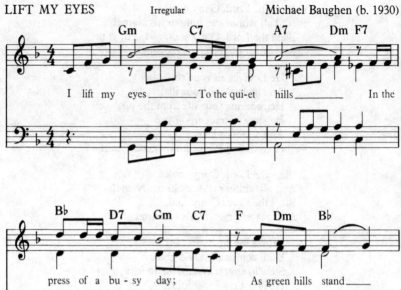

I lift my eyes___ To the qui-et hills___ In the

press of a bu-sy day; As green hills stand___

In a dus-ty land So God___ is my strength and stay.

1 I lift my eyes
   To the quiet hills
   In the press of a busy day;
   As green hills stand
   In a dusty land
   So God is my strength and stay.

2 I lift my eyes
   To the quiet hills
   To a calm that is mine to share;
   Secure and still
   In the Father's will
   And kept by the Father's care.

3 I lift my eyes
   To the quiet hills
   With a prayer as I turn to sleep;
   By day, by night,
   Through the dark and light
   My Shepherd will guard his sheep

4 I lift my eyes
   To the quiet hills
   And my heart to the Father's throne;
   In all my ways
   To the end of days
   The Lord will preserve his own.

TIMOTHY DUDLEY-SMITH (b. 1926)

# 138

# GOD IN THE PSALMS

KNOWLEDGE      8 7 8 7 D      Norman Warren (b. 1934)

1 Lord, you've tested me and known me,
   All of me is plain to you,
   Every purpose, every action,
   Seated, standing, lying down,
   Every thought my brain has fathomed,
   Every word my tongue pronounced,
   You surround me every moment,
   Lord, how wonderful you are.

2 Far beyond my meagre knowledge
   Is your character sublime.
   Can I flee your awesome presence
   Or escape beyond your power?
   Heaven, grave, the farthest wavecrest?
   In the darkness of the night?
   Still you find me, still you hold me,
   Lord.  ow wonderful you are.

3 Every inch of flesh and sinew,
   Every blood cell, every bone,
   From the hour of my conception,
   Planted in my mother's womb,
   You have fashioned me and formed me,
   Shaped and spun me, watched me grow,
   Inexhaustible your knowledge,
   Lord, how wonderful you are.

4 Rid us, Lord, of mischief makers,
   Tyrants, godless libertines,
   All who crush the course of justice,
   How I loathe such evil men!
   Search me too my God, and know me
   Keep me from the paths of sin,
   Watch me, lead me, try me, test me,
   Lord, how wonderful you are.

MICHAEL SAWARD (b. 1932)

# 139

SING A NEW SONG   7 6 7 6 and chorus   Norman Warren (b. 1934)

BASED ON *PSALM 149*

*Sing a new song, Hallelujah,*
*Sing aloud to God the King.*
*Let the saints of God adore him,*
*Let their joyful praises ring.*

1 Let instruments and voices
  Make music to the Lord;
  Be glad, O ransomed people,
  Rejoice with one accord.

2 The Lord accepts the service
  Of those who own his Name;
  He leads them on in triumph
  His greatness to proclaim.
    *Chorus*

3 They wield the word of justice,
  For God their hands are strong;
  They challenge men and nations,
  And fight all forms of wrong.

4 They work for truth and goodness,
  The noble and the right;
  And this will be their glory —
  To triumph in the fight.
    *Chorus*

J. E. SEDDON (b. 1915)

*The Chorus is not sung*
*after vvs. 1 & 3*

# INDEX TO FIRST LINE OF HYMNS
(First line of chorus in italics)

| | |
|---|---|
| 47 | *Alleluia, alleluia, give thanks* |
| 89 | All Scriptures are given |
| 101 | Almighty Father, great must be |
| 19 | A Man once came from Galilee |
| 64 | *And they'll know we are Christians* |
| 8 | Angels are bringing |
| 57 | As we break the bread |
| 22 | At the cross of Jesus |
| 7 | Bethlehem waiting |
| 136 | Bless the Lord, O my soul |
| 105 | *Blest are the poor in spirit* |
| 107 | Blest are the poor |
| 40 | Born by the Holy Spirit's breath |
| 72 | Christ is all the world's Good News |
| 9 | Christ is surely coming |
| 31 | Christ triumphant, ever reigning |
| 15 | Christ was born in Bethlehem |
| 12 | *Come and join the celebration* |
| 15 | *Come and praise the Lord our King* |
| 53 | Come, Christians, join to sing |
| 135 | *Come, rejoice before your Maker* |
| 131 | Come worship God who is worthy |
| 30 | Comes Mary to the grave |
| 23 | *Dance then wherever you may be* |
| 6 | Down to earth, as a dove |
| 26 | Do you see that man? |
| 76 | Earth is the Lord's, The |
| 87 | Faithful vigil ended |
| 115 | Father, although I cannot see |
| 86 | Father I will praise you |
| 60 | Father of all, with praise |
| 125 | Father on high to whom we pray |
| 41 | *Fear not, rejoice and be glad* |
| 41 | Fig tree is budding, The |
| 63 | Fire of God titanic Spirit |
| 119 | *Follow him, follow him* |
| 86 | *For as long as I have breath Lord* |
| 78 | For the fruits of his creation |
| 65 | Forth in the peace of Christ we go |
| 35 | For your gift of God the Spirit |

114 Give me, dear Lord, the power I need
85 Give me joy in my heart
46 *Glory, glory, hallelujah*
18 God is love: his the care
127 God is our strength and refuge
2 God of concrete, God of steel
110 God's spirit is in my heart
69 Go forth and tell! O Church of God
75 'Go forth!' The Lord's command
109 *Go tell it on the mountain*
13 Had he not loved us
14 *He came from the glory*
58 He gave his life in selfless love
102 He lives in us, the Christ of God
4 Here from all nations
110 *He sent me to give the good news*
48 Holy, holy, holy, holy
130 How lovely, how lovely, the place
23 I danced in the morning
103 I do not ask for life the whole way through
137 I lift my eyes
123 *I'm in the dance with him*
42 Indwelling Power, the promise
106 *In him there is no darkness at all*
121 In the long and lonely days
21 In the stillness of the night
70 In this age of noise and turmoil
123 I thought that freedom's dance
120 I want eternal life
106 I want to walk as a child of the light
119 I want to walk with Jesus Christ
16 Jesus Christ, Son of God
20 Jesus from glory to Bethlehem came
74 Jesus is King of Kings!
34 Jesus is Lord!
47 Jesus is Lord of all the earth
32 Jesus is the Lord of living
112 Jesus, Man who lived for others
28 Jesus, Prince and Saviour
17 Jesus our Lord, our King and our God
73 Jesus, we've prayed and we've read
134 Jubilate everybody
1 King of the universe

| | |
|---|---|
| 139 | Let instruments and voices |
| 82 | Let us all believe in the Lord |
| 88 | Let us for ever praise him |
| 45 | Let us praise God together |
| 6 | *Let us sing, sing, sing* |
| 132 | Let us sing to the God of salvation |
| 84 | Life has many rhythms, every heart |
| 96 | Light of the minds that know him |
| 129 | Listen to my prayer, Lord |
| 67 | Lord, as we rise to leave |
| 80 | Lord, for the years your love |
| 59 | Lord Jesus Christ |
| 77 | Lord made man, the Scriptures tell |
| 38 | Lord may we see |
| 97 | Lord of all hopefulness |
| 28 | *Lord of life triumphant* |
| 62 | Lord of the church, we pray |
| 24 | Lord of the cross of shame |
| 124 | Lord of the home, thine only Son |
| 17 | *Lord, we are called to follow you* |
| 71 | Lord, we have come |
| 138 | Lord, you've tested me and known me |
| 83 | Love is his word, love is his way |
| 111 | Make me a channel of your peace |
| 90 | May words of truth inform our minds |
| 117 | Men of God whose faith abounded |
| 128 | Merciful and gracious be |
| 92 | More precious than the finest gold |
| 43 | My Lord of light who made the worlds |
| 79 | Now join we, to praise the creator |
| 61 | Now let us from this table rise |
| 104 | Now let us learn of Christ |
| 109 | Oh Lord, when I was a seeker |
| 99 | O Lamb of God whose perfect love |
| 3 | O Lord of every shining constellation |
| 113 | O loving Lord, who art for ever seeking |
| 111 | *O Master, grant that I may never seek* |
| 10 | *O now carry me to Bethlehem* |
| 11 | O Son of God we too would gather |
| 46 | Our eyes have seen the glory |
| 94 | Our Father, who art in heaven |
| 21 | *O what a gift!* |

| 93 | Powerful in making us wise |
| 132 | *Praise our Maker* |
| 44 | Praise the Father, God of Justice |
| 50 | Praise the Lord in the rhythm |
| 54 | Praise the Lord, sing hallelujah! |
| 83 | *Richer than gold* |
| 122 | Search for the infant born in a stable |
| 10 | See him a-lying |
| 12 | See the shepherds hurry |
| 51 | Servants of God, the Almighty |
| 116 | Show me your measured plan, O Lord |
| 105 | Show us your ways, O Lord |
| 18 | *Sing aloud, loud, loud* |
| 139 | *Sing a new song, Hallelujah* |
| 85 | *Sing hosanna! Sing hosanna!* |
| 133 | Sing to God new songs of worship |
| 36 | *Spirit of God, unseen as the wind* |
| 108 | Tell out, my soul |
| 27 | These are the facts |
| 29 | This day above all days |
| 126 | This earth belongs to God |
| 81 | This is the day |
| 95 | This morning as I wait on thee |
| 49 | Thou art worthy |
| 14 | Virgin Mary had a baby boy, The |
| 52 | We are come into his house |
| 64 | We are one in the Spirit |
| 56 | We come as guests invited |
| 66 | We have a gospel to proclaim |
| 55 | *We really want to thank you, Lord* |
| 25 | Were you there when they crucified my Lord? |
| 98 | We seek, dear Lord, your presence |
| 55 | We thank you Lord, for your gift |
| 79 | We thank you, O God, for your goodness |
| 37 | We went with a message |
| 39 | When God the Spirit came |
| 68 | When the Church of Jesus |
| 5 | When the sun is darkened |
| 100 | When to our world the Saviour came |
| 33 | Who is Jesus? |
| 126 | *Who may go up the hill of the Lord* |
| 91 | World you made is full of words, The |
| 118 | Your love, O Christ, is near to me |
| 36 | You spoke to men |

## AUTHORS

| | |
|---|---|
| Abbot, Eileen | 42, 75 |
| Appleford, Patrick | 17, 59 |
| | |
| Ballinger, Bruce | 52 |
| Barnes, Jonathan | 130 |
| Bateman, C. E. | 53 |
| Baughen, M. A. | 89, 133, 135, 136 |
| Bayly, Albert | 3, 124 |
| Beaumont, Gerard | 107 |
| Bewes, Richard | 127, 132 |
| Burns, Edward J. | 66, 74 |
| Butler, P. C. | 109 |
| | |
| Cansdale, J. H. | 71 |
| Carter, Sydney | 23 |
| Casey, Peter | 26, 50, 121 |
| Clarkson, Margaret | 35, 54 |
| Collison, Valerie | 12 |
| Connaughton, Luke | 83 |
| | |
| Dale, Alan | 110 |
| Dearmer, Percy | 18 |
| Dudley-Smith, Timothy | 13, 28, 29, 32, 33, 39, 40, 56, 62, 77, 80, 87, 96, 100, 108, 125, 128, 137 |
| | |
| Eddison, John | 22, 92, 95, 98, 103, 114, 115 |
| | |
| 'Fishermen', The | 55 |
| | |
| Glandfield, John | 51 |
| | |
| Hartropp, Derek | 82 |
| Hewlett, Michael | 37 |
| Hews, Michael | 16, 91 |
| Hews, Michael *with* David Lewis and Rikki Sefton | 123 |
| Houghton, S. I. | 120 |
| Howard, Pat Uhl | 21 |
| | |
| Idle, Christopher | 4, 5, 8, 9, 43, 72, 93, 104, 117, 126 |
| | |
| Jones, Richard | 2 |

Kaan, Fred                          6, 57, 61, 67, 81

Lewis, David *with*
    Michael Hews and
    Rikki Sefton                    123
Luttrell, Beth                      70

Mansell, David                      34
Meredith, Roland                    46
Metcalf, Michael                    79
Mowbray, David                      60, 101

Old, Margaret                       19, 36
Owens, J. & C.                      48

Pavey, Ron                          99
Perry, Michael                      10, 30, 44, 102, 131, 134
Porter, David                       88
Porteous, Christopher               7, 11, 38, 58, 118
Pratt Green, F.                     68, 78, 84

Quinn, James                        65

Reith, Angela                       73
Routley, Erik                       76

Saward, Michael                     1, 24, 27, 31, 63, 138
Scholtes, Peter                     64
Seddon, J. E.                       20, 45, 69, 129, 139
Sefton, Rikki *with*
    Michael Hews and
    David Lewis                     123
Slack, Kenneth                      112
Smail, Tom                          49
Smith, M.                           86
Struthers, Jan                      97

Thomerson, Kathleen                 106
Tongeman, Peter                     90, 116

Vaughan Jenkins, William            113

Ward, Roy                           122

## COMPOSERS, SOURCES OF TUNES, ARRANGERS
(Numbers italicised refer to arrangements)

| | |
|---|---|
| Appleford, Patrick | 17, 51, 59 |
| Austin, David | 92 (2nd) |
| | |
| Bach, J. C. | 117 (melody) |
| Bach, J. S. | *56* (adapted and harmonised by) |
| Baggett, Ed | 55 |
| Baughen, Michael | 31, 69, 71, 89, 108 (1st), 136, 137 |
| Baughen, Michael *with* | |
|    David Wilson | 20, 80 |
| Beaumont, Gerard | 107 |
| Beethoven, L.v. | 133 |
| Blunt, Frederick | 22 (1st) |
| Bristol, Lee H. | 124 |
| Buck, Percy | 101 |
| Butler, P. C. | *109* |
| Butler, P. C. *with* | |
|    David Wilson | *15* |
| | |
| *Calhoun melody* | 45 |
| Carter, Paul | 122 |
| Carter, Sydney | *23* |
| *Chants Ordinaires de* | |
|    *l'Office Divin* | 33 |
| Clarke, Jeremiah | 126 |
| Coates, Eric | 127 |
| Coates, Stephen | *10, 131, 134* |
| Collison, Valerie | 12 |
| Cooke, David *with* | |
|    Judy Mackenzie | 91 |
| Crawshaw, D. J. | *14* |
| *'The Crucifixion' (Stainer)* | 35, 44 |
| | |
| Davies, William | 112 |
| Durden, Alastair | *36* |
| Dykes, J. B. | 42, 113 |
| | |
| *Edric Connor Collection* | 14 |
| Elliott, James W. | 100 |

| | |
|---|---|
| English Folk Melody | 43 |
| Ferguson, W. H. | 9, 96 |
| Filitz, Friedrich | 129 |
| Fishel, Don | 47 |
| *French Church Melody* | 33 |
| *Gaelic Melody* | 7 (1st), 8 |
| Gale, Yvonne | 86 |
| Gardiner's *Sacred Melodies* | 40 (2nd), 66 |
| Greatorex, Walter | 108 (2nd) |
| *Harmonischer Liederschatz* | 60 |
| Harris, William H. | 103 |
| Hartropp, Derek | 82 |
| Harvey, Roger | *82* |
| Hassler, Hans | 56 (melody) |
| Hatton, J. | 65 (attrib. to) |
| Havergal, W. H. | *60* |
| Holst, Gustav | *18* |
| Houghton, S. I. | 120 |
| Howard, Pat Uhl | 21 |
| Humphris, Ian | 92 (1st) |
| *Irish Traditional Melody* | 11, 62, 73, 97 |
| Jenkins, David | 98 |
| Jones, James E. | 95 (2nd) |
| Knecht, J. H. | 88 |
| *La Feillée, Methode* | 4 (1st) |
| *Lancashire Folk Song* | 32 |
| Leach, Anthony | *16, 90,* 95 (1st), 116 |
| Llewellyn, William | 105 |
| Lockley, John | *26,* 121 |
| Lvov, A. | 1 |
| Mackenzie, Judy *with* David Cooke | 91 |
| *'The Magic Flute'* (*Mozart*) | 99 |
| Mansell, David J. | 34 |
| Maries, Andrew | 58 |

| | |
|---|---|
| Martin, G. C. | 125 |
| Maynard, John | 37 |
| Metcalf, Michael | 79 |
| Milner, Anthony | 83 |
| Mills, Pauline | 49 |
| Mozart, W. A. | 99 |
| | |
| *Negro Spiritual* | 25 |
| Nicholson, Sidney | *33* (harmonised by) |
| | |
| Osborne, Leslie | 50 |
| Owens, Jimmy | 48 |
| | |
| Parry, Hubert | 38 |
| Perry, Michael | 10, 131, 134 |
| Pratt Green, F. | 68 |
| *Piae Cantiones* (melody from) | 18 |
| Prichard, R. H. | 63 (melody) |
| Pulkingham, Betty | *21, 47, 55, 111, 119* |
| | |
| Reith, Angela | *25, 91,* 123 |
| Reith, Angela *with* | |
|   Robin Sheldon | *78* |
| Richards, Hubert | 110 |
| Routley, Erick | 53, 67, *73* (harmonised by), 76, *97* (harmonised by) |
| | |
| Scholtes, Peter | 64 |
| *Scottish Folk Song* | 36 |
| *Scottish Melody* | 90 |
| *Shaker Tune* | 23 |
| Sharpe, Evelyn *and others* | 57 |
| Shaw, Geoffrey | *77* |
| Shaw, Martin | 74, 75 |
| Sheldon, Robin | *11,* 22 (2nd), 29, *32,* 39, *43, 46, 48* (alt. version), *52, 62, 71,* 84, *94, 99,* 104, *113* (harmonised by), 115, *126, 127,* 133 |
| Sheldon, Robin *with* | |
|   Angela Reith | *78* |
| Smart, Henry | 54 |
| Smith, Alfred | 13 |

| | |
|---|---|
| Smith, Isaac | 114 |
| Stainer, John | 35 (1st), 44, 72 |
| Stoodley, Rob | *121* |
| Sullivan, Arthur | 28 |
| *Swiss Folk Tune* | 119 |
| *Swiss Traditional Melody* | 61 |
| | |
| Temple, Sebastian | 111 |
| Terry, Richard | 3 |
| Thalben-Ball, G. | *38* |
| Thatcher, Reginald | 81 |
| Thomas, Alan | 26 |
| Thomerson, Kathleen | 106 |
| Thrupp, Joseph | 4 (2nd), 27, 93 |
| *Traditional* | 15, 16, 46, 78, 85, 94, 109, 132 |
| Tredinnick, Noel | 40 (1st), 135 (2nd) |
| Turle, James | 102 |
| *Tyrolean Melody* | 19 |
| | |
| Vaughan Williams, R. | 24 |
| Vick, Beryl | 70 |
| | |
| Warren, Norman | 5, 30, 128, *132, 134, 135* (1st), 138, 139 |
| Watson, Sydney | 35 (2nd) |
| Westbrook, Francis | 2 |
| White, Jack Noble | *64* (harmonised by) |
| Wickham, Helen | 7 (2nd), 118 |
| Wilson, David | *45*, 87, 130, 135 (1st), *136* |
| Wilson, David *with* Michael Baughen | 20, 80 |
| Wilson, David *with* P. C. Butler | *15* |
| Wooldridge, W. | *89* |
| Wright, Priscilla | 41 |

# ALPHABETICAL LIST OF TUNES

to which the words are set in the music editions of *Songs of Worship.*

| | |
|---|---|
| Abridge | 114 |
| Advent Psalm | 5 |
| Alberta | 103 |
| All Believe | 82 |
| Alleluia | 47 |
| All Scriptures | 89 |
| All Through The Night | 78 |
| | |
| Baby Boy | 14 |
| Balmoral | 112 |
| Barbara Allen | 43 |
| Battle Hymn | 46 |
| Bayswater | 95 (1st) |
| Beatitudes | 105 |
| Birling | 77 |
| Bless The Lord | 136 |
| Blest Are The Poor | 107 |
| Bunessan | 7 (1st), 8 |
| | |
| Calypso Carol | 10 |
| Capitol Heights | 70 |
| Caswall | 129 |
| Celebrations | 12 |
| Charity | 72 |
| Choral Symphony | 133 |
| Christ Triumphant | 31 |
| Church Triumphant | 100 |
| Come And Praise | 15 |
| Come Rejoice (1 and 2) | 135 |
| Comes Mary | 30 |
| Cotton Weaver | 32 |
| Cresswell | 83 |
| Cross of Jesus | 35 (1st), 44 |
| Cuddesdon | 9 |
| | |
| Dam Busters' March | 127 |
| Day of the Spirit | 37 |
| Days of Jesus | 7 (2nd) |
| Do You See That Man? | 26 |
| Down Ampney | 24 |

| | |
|---|---|
| Downland | 115 |
| Duke Street | 65 |
| Epiphany Hymn | 4 (2nd), 27 |
| Faithful Vigil | 87 |
| Finest Gold | 92 (1st) |
| Franconia | 60 |
| Freedom Song | 123 |
| Fulda | 40 (2nd), 66 |
| Giving And Keeping | 120 |
| God's Spirit | 110 |
| Go Forth | 69 |
| Gonfalon Royal | 101 |
| Goodwin-Hudson | 116 |
| Go, Tell | 109 |
| Grafton | 33 |
| Green Hill | 22 (2nd) |
| Growing | 104 |
| Henfield | 17 |
| Here From All Nations | 4 (1st) |
| Highwood | 3 |
| His House | 52 |
| Holy Faith | 125 |
| Holy, Holy | 48 |
| Honeycomb | 92 (2nd) |
| How Lovely | 130 |
| Hyfrydol | 63 |
| Invitation To Worship | 131 |
| I Want To Walk | 106 |
| Jerusalem | 38 |
| Jesus From Glory | 20 |
| Jesus Is Lord | 34 |
| Jonathan | 84 |
| Jubilate Everybody | 134 |
| Julius | 75 |
| Knecht | 88 |
| Knowledge | 138 |
| Let Us Praise | 45 |
| Let Us Sing | 6 |

| | |
|---|---|
| Lift My Eyes | 137 |
| Little Cornard | 74 |
| Living Lord | 59 |
| Londonderry Air | 11, 62 |
| Long and Lonely Days | 121 |
| Lord of Lords | 16 |
| Lord of the Dance | 23 |
| Lord of the Years | 71, 80 |
| Lyndhurst | 22 (1st) |
| May Hill | 35 (2nd) |
| Merciful and Gracious | 128 |
| Mo Ranch | 53 |
| Mozart | 99 |
| New Hope | 76 |
| New Horizons | 2 |
| Northbrook | 81 |
| Now Join We | 79 |
| O Quanta Qualia | 4 |
| One In The Spirit | 64 |
| Our Father | 94 |
| Passion Chorale | 56 |
| Penlan | 98 |
| Platts Lane | 57 |
| Praise The Lord | 50 |
| Redeemer | 86 |
| Regent Square | 54 |
| Rejoice And Be Glad | 41 |
| Russian Anthem | 1 |
| Search For The Infant | 122 |
| Selfless Love | 58 |
| Servants Of God | 51 |
| Sing A New Song | 139 |
| Sing Hosanna | 85, 132 |
| Skye Boat Song | 36 |
| Slane | 73, 97 |
| Solothurn | 61 |
| Somerset Hills | 124 |
| Sound Of Wind | 29, 39 |
| St. Francis | 111 |

St. Gertrude                28
St. Leonard                117
Strength And Stay          42, 113
Sursum Corda               13
Sutton Trinity             68

Tell Out My Soul           108 (1st)
Thank You, Lord            55
Theodoric                  18
Thou Art Worthy            49
Trumpet Voluntary          126
Tyrol                      19

Walden                     95 (2nd)
Walking                    119
Wansbeck                   67
Were You There             25
Westminster                102
What A Gift                21
Whitsun Psalm              40 (1st)
Wolvercote                 96
Woodlands                  108 (2nd)
Words                      91

Ye Banks And Braes         90
Your Love                  118

# METRICAL INDEX

| | | | |
|---|---|---|---|
| SM | 60 | 85.85 | 94 |
| CM | 95, 102 | 868.78 | 134 |
| | 114, 116 | 86.86.86 | 115 |
| CM+refrain | 36 | 86.86.886 | 92 |
| DCM | 19 | 8787 | 35, 43, 44, |
| LM | 40, 61, 65 | | 112, 135 |
| | 66, 77, 90 | 8787.D | 63, 70, |
| | 100, 101, | | 133, 138 |
| | 124 | 87.87.77 | 117 |
| DLM | 38 | 87.87.87 | 32, 33, 54 |
| 5664 | 57 | 88+refrain | 47 |
| 6565 | 22(ii), 87, | 884.D | 118 |
| | 129 | 8888 (swing) | 82 |
| 6565D | 9, 22(i), 68, | 88.88.88 | 99, 125 |
| | 84 | 88.97.10.7 | 83 |
| 6565 triple | 28 | 8.12.15.8 | 48 |
| 6665D | 37 | 98.98 | 79 |
| 6666 | 104 | 98.98D | 76 |
| 6666+refrain | 6 | 10.4.10.4.10.10 | 103 |
| 6666D | 53 | 10.7.10.8 | 20 |
| 6666+refrain | 18 | 10.7.10.8+refrain | 106 |
| 66.66.88 | 74 | 10.8.10.8 | 26 |
| 6675 | 16 | 10.8.10.9+refrain | 85 |
| 6686D | 107 | 10.9.10.9+refrain | 132 |
| 6686.66 | 29, 39 | 10.10.9+refrain | 14 |
| 66.11.D | 24 | 10.10.10.10 | 13, 69, 75, |
| 67711 | 30 | | 108 |
| 6968+refrain | 126 | 10.10.11.11 | 51 |
| 74.84.884 | 78 | 10.10.14.10 | 25 |
| 764.D7676 | 52 | 10.11.11.12 | 73, 97 |
| 7676 | 88 | 11.10.11.9 | 50 |
| 7676D | 56, 96, 98 | 11.10.11.10 | 1, 3, 4, 27, |
| 7676+refrain | 139 | | 42, 71, 80, |
| 7775 | 72 | | 81, 93, |
| 777578.11 | 127 | | 113, 131 |
| 77.77.77 | 2, 128 | 11.10.11.10.D | 11, 62 |
| | | 11.11+refrain | 15 |
| 847.847 | 5 | 11.11.11.5 | 67 |

| | |
|---|---|
| 11.12.11.12+refrain | 34 |
| 11.14+refrain | 12 |
| 12.11.12.11 | 130 |
| 14.14.6+refrain | 46 |
| 14.14.14.14 | 58 |
| Irregular | 7, 8, 10, |
| | 17, 21, 23 |
| | 31, 41, 45 |
| | 49, 55, 59, |
| | 64, 86, 89, |
| | 91, 105, |
| | 109, 110, |
| | 111, 119, |
| | 120, 121 |
| | 122, 123, |
| | 136, 137 |